THE PLAGUE KILLERS

William C. Gorgas (center) *leading the attack on yellow fever in Guatemala*

The Plague Killers

GREER WILLIAMS

Charles Scribner's Sons • *New York*

Frontispiece photograph courtesy of the Rockefeller
Foundation; conversion by Joseph Stanley

A book, to the lover of books, may constitute a treasury of ideas, facts, experience, or adventure but is a limited method of communication. It may not be read by persons most in need of the information it offers. I should like, for instance, to see the message in the present book delivered to the prime ministers of the small and great nations of the world, on the assumption that all are not familiar with the words attributed to a great prime minister, Benjamin Disraeli, during Parliamentary debate of the Public Health Act of 1875:

"The public health is the foundation on which repose the happiness of the people and the power of a country. The care of public health is the first duty of a statesman."

Reading history, we are forced to conclude that many rulers of nations are, by Disraeli's definition, badly educated or not statesmen. History has much to say about prime ministers, presidents, kings, generals, and dictators, but makes little reference to the health of the people. Nor does the general historian concern himself with the impact of disease on the course of human events. Hans Zinsser pointed this out in his *Rats, Lice, and History*.

Pick up any general history book. Do you find the words "health" or "public health" in the index? You may find fleeting references in the text to "medicine" and its scientific advances, but not much about human illness. Very little is reported in history books about the quality and quantity of human life at any stage, about how people felt, how long they lived, and what effects such vital statistics had on civilization's progress. You can find mention of the Black Death and other plagues that from time to time swept through the population and upset the ambitions of politicians and generals. But there is little interest in human well-being, whether people were cold and hungry, stiff with arthritis, or filled with anxiety, whether they were bitten by mosquitoes or covered with flies, spit up blood, had a sharp pain in the chest, burned with fever, or suffered from headaches and dizzy spells.

This is what health science, method, and organization are about.

We cannot blame the historians, of course, if the power struggle pre-empted their attention. Human conflict distracts us all. Yet we may be sure that people always have been concerned about health. Why is it that public health did not make history, at least until modern times? First, people in good health do not think about it, any more than the individual with excellent digestion is conscious of his gastrointestinal tract; good health means freedom from illness. Second, and probably more important, bad health—like the weather—was something our forefathers could do little about. The intervention of the physician, the priest, or magician might be welcome in a crisis, but it was readily apparent that the results were not too good. Until the emergence of a science of medicine in the twentieth century, the general historian had little to talk about *in health terms*. The events that occupied him were mostly of a political, economic, or social influence on human well-being, the most obvious being acts of violence.

It was wholly predictable that man would take an increased interest in his health in the twentieth century, following new and startling insights into the causes, transmission, and prevention of infectious diseases. Frederick T. Gates, an important force in the establishment of both the Rockefeller Institute for Medical Research and the Rockefeller Foundation, became convinced in the early 1900's that, as medical science advanced, public health services could be organized to prevent disease, the health of people would improve, their capacity to learn would increase, and their ability to make a living would be greatly enhanced. Not only deaths but all sickness, he believed, would decline and there would be less need for doctors and hospitals. Like other enthusiastic crusaders for health through science, Gates spoke of some distant time when most of mankind would enjoy freedom from disease and achieve, as he said, "universal health." Nothing resembling such an achievement exists today.

The Rockefeller Foundation's international health staff—first called a Commission, then a Board, and finally a Division—ranged over the world for thirty-eight years. The International Health Division had one practical purpose in mind: to get people and their governments interested in preventing disease. The Rockefeller men offered help in getting programs started. Where welcome, they took up residence and stayed a while, sometimes for years.

This staff, usually numbering seventy to eighty—a few of its members women—sought and found opportunities to improve the health of the masses and were participants with seventy-five cooperating governments in efforts that met varying success in reducing the hazards of twenty-one specific diseases or health problems, including tuberculosis, yaws, rabies, influenza, typhus, amebiasis, schistosomiasis, dysentery, typhoid fever, hepatitis, undulant fever, and nutritional deficiencies. But most of all they were the protagonists, often prime movers, in the campaigns against hookworm disease, malaria, and yellow fever.

The campaigns against these three diseases have been selected as the dramatic vehicle by which the work of the International Health Division, sprawling across both hemispheres, in both the temperate and tropical world, and over four decades in time, can be reduced to a book of readable length and some popular appeal. This necessitates the nearly total neglect of some of the I.H.D.'s other major interests, particularly of its promotion of rural health services and support of professional education and training for public health doctors and public health nurses.

From 1913 through 1950, the Foundation allocated nearly $100 million to health activities, the largest amount, about $33 million, being for schools of public health, schools of nursing, 2,566 fellowships, and other training expenses. More than $22 million went into the operating costs of the field staff and its offices. Aid in the development of state and local health services in the United States and abroad totaled more than $8 million. The laboratories of the I.H.D. at the Rockefeller Institute required nearly $3 million. The activities of the Rockefeller Foundation Health Commission during World War II took $2 million. The Health Organization of the League of Nations received nearly $1 million between World Wars I and II.

In a total of $22 million spent for the control and investigation of specific diseases, the four principal items were yellow fever, $8 million; malaria, $4.5 million; hookworm disease, $3.8 million; tuberculosis, $3 million.

Compared to the far larger amounts that participating governments were stimulated to spend on public health, or by modern technical assistance standards, the sums of money expended by the Rockefeller Foundation were small. As Raymond B. Fosdick, Foundation president from 1936 to 1948, often remarked, it was the men and not the money that counted, though of course it must be recognized that without the money the men would not have had the opportunity to test their abilities in Latin America, Asia, Africa, and southern Europe.

There were more than four hundred on the field staff of the International Health Division throughout its history—public health physicians, nurses, engineers, entomologists, bacteriologists, and others. The special place that they won in the hearts of foreign peoples still emerges spontaneously in comments at international health meetings and elsewhere, as well as in published statements.

The grass-roots attitude was everywhere the same, and no better illustrated than in the anecdote about Dr. John M. Weir, now director of the Foundation's Medical and Natural Sciences program. Weir was making a morbidity survey in Egypt when the chief of an Arab village informed him one day: "We have decided not to kill you."

"That's nice," said Weir agreeably.

An explanation was forthcoming: "We were going to stone you to death because your country is friendly to Israel, which is our enemy, but we know you are from the Rockefeller Foundation and are here to do good, so we will spare you."

The doctor was glad to have this endorsement and said he would pass it on to his superiors. He knew the volatile Arabs too well to believe that the chief was joking. The British bacteriologist who worked with Weir was less fortunate. A mob pulled him from his car, stoned him to death, and tore his body limb from limb.

GREER WILLIAMS

Hingham, Massachusetts

Contents

PART THREE: COSTLY VICTORY—YELLOW FEVER

THE PLAGUE KILLERS

I

THE HOOKWORM DOCTORS

1

The Laziness Bug

In the second half of the twentieth century it is hard to believe that there was a time when the basic idea of the campaign against hookworm disease—"helping people help themselves"—was novel and daring. What may surprise even public health historians, is that the roots of international health as an action program, as a demonstration of how people in different parts of the world can work together, are to be found in the American South. Yet this interpretation is unescapable, even though the first action took place entirely within the United States. In view of the hostility following the North's defeat of the South, as well as of the social and cultural differences between the two regions, the Mason-Dixon line—while not an international boundary—was deeply etched in public imagination as something to be crossed.

The public campaign against hookworm was a joke when it began, even though the disease rivaled malaria as a major misery of people in the South. There it was an endemic, ever-present destroyer of life and health. Before 1900, however, the existence of hookworm infection in the United States was not known to more than one or two physicians and one zoologist named Charles Wardell Stiles (1867-1941). Dr. Stiles was the son of a Methodist minister. He attended school in Hartford, where he led his class in languages. He had an explanation for this. His Methodist grandfather held that there were only three ways a boy might properly spend his Sundays: reading the Bible, singing hymns, or walking in the churchyard. Stiles chose the Bible, and after reading it in English diverted himself by reading it in French, Latin, Greek, German, and Italian. His family wanted him to become a clergyman, but he never could learn enough, it seemed, about the insects, reptiles, and small mammals of Connecticut. At nineteen, he went to Europe to study medical zoology in Berlin, Leipzig, Trieste, and Paris.

From European physicians he learned what there was to be known about hookworms. Helminthologists, a tiny, vanishing group of scientists who devote their careers to studying worms, will tell you that worms of various kinds have been the bosom—no, abdominal—companions of primitive people throughout the nearly one million years human beings have been in existence. Worms parasitic on man fall into three important groups: roundworms, tapeworms, and flukes. These, in their adult form, range in length from a few hundredths of an inch to 30 feet in the case of the fish tapeworm. The best-known disease producers are the round, hook, whip, pin, and filarial (thread) forms. The vast majority of worms infesting man inhabit the intestine, the most common being *Ascaris*, the large roundworm (6 to 14 inches long). The second most common and probably the most troublesome of all is the hookworm; it reaches a length of 4/10 to 5/10 inch.

Something like half the world's population lives in the hookworm belt extending around the globe between

36° north latitude and 30° south latitude. In this area, hookworms are one of the great retarding influences in community development, for these parasites live in the small intestines of nearly half the population.

Nature imposes fantastically complicated conditions on hookworms in their struggle for survival. They exist only where soil, moisture, and temperature occur in the right combination. The soil must be sandy or loamy, not clay or muck. The rainfall needs to be more than 40 inches a year, and the mean annual temperature over 50°. On the other hand, the hookworm larva cannot survive long in water or sun.

The hookworm is totally dependent for survival on man's infinite capacity for fouling his own nest, in this instance, mainly for fecal pollution of the ground he walks on. Any contact of his skin with hookworm-infested soil might suffice for infection, but for the most part human hookworm disease depends on man's going barefoot; this is the disease of the barefoot boy.

The worm's life cycle is as follows: the male and somewhat larger female hook themselves to the intestinal wall and suck blood over a life span that may continue for years. At some point that does not seem to have been captured in medical literature, the male unhooks, finds, and mates with the female. Thereafter the female may lay from 5,000 to 20,000 eggs a day, depending on her species. The host's daily bowel movement brings these eggs to earth, where under favorable conditions they hatch into rod-shaped larvae about 1/100 inch long. The larva feeds on bacteria, molts twice, almost doubles its size, and becomes a threadlike worm. This tiny worm now can sustain life without food for as long as a month or more. It is excitable and aggressive when the ground is warm and wet—when the dew is on the grass—and can lash its way for a few inches upward or sideward through moist soil and along blades of grass covered with a water film.

The larva's sole objective in life is to find its way "back home"—some species prefer cats, dogs, or other animals, but two species prey on man. The journey begins when by blind chance the larva makes contact with the bare skin, through which it is equipped to bore, like a corkscrew, with surprising ease. It prefers the tender skin between the toes.

Once inside, the worm may make a lucky or an unlucky turn. It may enter a lymph gland, part of the body's general defense system; if so, it will be trapped and killed. But if it enters a blood vessel, it can be carried alive through the circulation and pumped through the heart to the lungs. There, in an alveolus, or air sac where the blood absorbs inhaled air, the worm makes another break and thence is pushed upward through the bronchial tubes, by the cilia, or drainage system, into the windpipe and throat. Here it could make another unlucky turn, be coughed outside, and have to begin again, but ordinarily it descends the gastrointestinal tract through normal swallowing action. Once in the small intestine, the worm bites into the mucous membrane lining and makes itself at home. It drinks blood voraciously and quickly matures.

For its size, about half the length of a pin, one adult worm can extract an amazing amount of its host's blood in a day's time. If the person were not making blood to replace his loss, from 150 to 1,000 worms would bleed him dry in about twenty-five weeks. One expert estimated that the human race's daily blood loss to hookworms is equivalent to the exsanguination of 1,500,000 persons per day.

Anemia is the primary danger in hookworm disease. The anemia is of a simple iron-deficiency type due to a decrease of red blood cells. The worm lives on the plasma and excretes the red cells. The infected person can readily make more blood but cannot replace lost iron, except by taking iron medically. A person who is well fed and has a balanced diet can better withstand a hookworm attack than one who gets little to eat or whose diet lacks iron.

Some people may harbor some hookworms all their lives without too much trouble. They are classed as carriers—infected, but not seriously diseased. Their skin may have become a little pale and dry and even acquired a yellowish tinge. They may have stomach aches and their hearts may race a bit with exertion. Their muscles may be weak and they may show distaste for work. This is a very light infection, by probably no more than 25 to 100 worms.

In moderately severe cases, with 100 to 500 worms, the classic hookworm syndrome may emerge. The person feels, looks, and acts sick. His skin may be a dirty yellow, like tallow. He is depressed, reacts passively to his surroundings, and appears stupid. His stomach may bother him constantly, with nausea and some vomiting and alternate bouts of constipation and diarrhea. His heart is slightly enlarged, his pulse rapid but weak, and he may feel dizzy. His chest aches, his head aches, his joints ache, his feet may "go to sleep." He can work only with the greatest of effort, and then becomes breathless and quickly exhausted.

Now there also appears one of the surest signs of hookworm disease. The victim may have a voracious appetite and eat dirt and other strange things, mainly mineral in character. This being considered rather bizarre and depraved behavior, he seldom will admit it.

In severe cases, the heart becomes much enlarged, as it attempts to make up for the intensified anemia by pumping faster. The patient may lose his nervous reflexes and have crawling sensations, his ankles may swell, and a second classic sign may appear—a pot belly. Turn him around and he may present a third sign—"angel's wings," a protuberance of the shoulder blades due to the figure-S slump of his emaciated body. With red cells from 10 to 30 percent of normal, with blurred vision, muscles painful to the touch, irregular fever, a melancholic facial expression, and "fish eye" stare, he is truly in a debilitated condition because of his 500, 1,000, or more hookworms, and may die of any secondary infection. Hookworm is not in itself a major cause of death but is frequently a contributory factor in fatalities from other diseases.

Hookworm disease reaches its highest frequency and severity in children, and whether it kills them or not it can wreck their lives. It arrests both physical and mental development. A child with a persistent infection in his growing years by his teens may look five to ten years younger than he is. He may be near the bottom of his class in school or unable to attend school at all. Hookworm infection delays puberty and may produce sexual impotence in men and cessation of menstruation in women.

One attack of hookworm does not immunize man against a second attack, as occurs with many diseases caused by bacteria or viruses. However, people living in areas where the soil is infested acquire some resistance or achieve a biological truce with their invaders. Many, though not all, helminthologists concede the operation of some kind of immunity factor but regard hookworm as a self-limiting infection that becomes a threat to human health and life only in the presence of a dietary deficiency including a lack of sufficient iron. The best example of acquired resistance—the experts refuse to describe it as a racial immunity—is found in the Negro, who is less often infected and carries his worm burden more lightly than the white man.

The scientific names for hookworm are: *Uncinaria* (from Latin: *uncus:* hook) or *Ancylostoma* (Greek: bent mouth). Charles Stiles noted that earlier observers got the hook on the wrong end. To them the two riblike structures in the tail of the male looked like hooks, but these are actually part of a "copulatory bursa," or purse, the male implement of genital union with the female. Eventually the four hooklike teeth in the suckerlike mouth were taken into account.

Italian physicians, in the mid-nineteenth century, were the first to connect the worms with the disease. In Europe it was called "miner's anemia," in Egypt, the "green sickness" (chlorosis), and in Brazil, "tropical anemia." The Italians showed that hookworm disease could be diagnosed in living persons from the distinctive ova, or eggs, passed in the feces. Thus began the long, tedious, repugnant, but indispensable scatology of hookworm diagnosis: the collection of stool specimens, microscopic examination, and eventually the methodologically exacting count of the number of eggs in a gram of feces.

Some physicians doubted the cause. The clinching evidence came when it was discovered that the anemia could be cured with a vermifuge that expelled the worms. The first specific treatment was thymol, a crystalline derivative of phenol (carbolic acid). It was unpleasant but in a 1.5 percent solution did not seem to bother the patients otherwise. Thymol became the accepted treatment.

American doctors were unaware of all this, but Stiles deduced that hookworm disease was probably to be found in the American states bordering on the Gulf of Mexico, even though neither the worm nor the disease seemed to have been definitely recognized in this region. Back in the United States in 1891, he became consulting zoologist in the Bureau of Animal Industry of the Department of Agriculture in Washington. As an incidental duty, he was custodian of the helminthological collection of the National Museum. Looking over the specimens of American parasites, he was surprised to find no specimen of hookworm.

He looked into American medical literature and found nothing definite. There were many references, to be sure, to "chronic anemia" and "continuous malaria" associated with dirt-eating, a phenomenon well known in the South and occasionally the subject of shocker feature stories in Sunday newspapers. People ate dirt, clay, brick, resin, and were considered morally degenerate for doing so. A popular assumption was that they did so to make themselves sick and thus get out of work. A common remedy in Florida was said to be whisky or cider in which nails had been steeped.

With his European training, Stiles knew that dirt-eating and hookworm disease were diagnostically inseparable and he said as much in his lectures on worms to medical students at Johns Hopkins. Dr. William Osler (1849-1919) took him to task, maintaining that a disease as easily recognized as hookworm could not be so generally overlooked. If the great Osler, one of American medicine's heroes, disbelieved Stiles, then who could blame 20,000 doctors in the Southern states if they did likewise? Furthermore, as some were to point out, he was not an M.D. but only an Sc.D.

Nonetheless, Stiles ended every lecture from 1892 to 1897 with these words: "Gentlemen, if you find cases of anemia in man in the tropics or subtropics, the cause of which is not clear to you, consider the possibility of hookworm disease; make a microscopic examination of the feces and look for eggs."

The first pay-off of his perseverance came while Stiles was out of the country for two years, as scientific attaché in the American Embassy in Germany. One of his students had been Dr. Bailey K. Ashford (1873-1934) who became an Army medical officer and accompanied the first troops to Puerto Rico in the Spanish-American War. Ashford was casually struck by the appearance of many of the peons from the sugar and coffee plantations. They were pale, emaciated, listless. In 1899, a catastrophic hurricane hit Puerto Rico. Ashford, in charge of a relief hospital, now saw the sickly looking Puerto Ricans at clinical close range. Three out of four, he found, were anemic. They had been living on sugar cane, but did not improve when given rice, beans, and codfish, plus iron. Ashford excluded malaria and pondered the high eosinophilia, characteristic of hookworm disease, in his patients' blood tests. There is nothing too esoteric about this finding. Eosin is a rose-colored dye and eosinophils are blood cells readily stained by the dye. They suggest a sensitivity reaction such as occurs in infection with animal parasites.

Ashford looked for hookworm eggs in his patients' fecal specimens and found them by the thousands. With thymol capsules followed by Epsom salts, he worked what to the peons' viewpoint was pure magic. His treatment relieved the anemia. In April 1900, he became the first to report the presence of hookworm disease in Puerto Rico.

Returning to Washington in January, before publication of his findings, Ashford took a bottle of his worms to Stiles's laboratory, but the zoologist was still in Berlin. Ashford told Stiles's assistant that "there was something curious about the worms." Ashford left the bottle with the Army Medical Museum, his curiosity unsatisfied. Stiles returned to the Bureau of Animal Industry later that year. In 1901, he received a bottle of worms from a physician in Galveston, Texas, who had examined eighty-odd medical students at the University of Texas and found hookworms in eight. Studying these worms under the microscope, Stiles saw that they were different from *Ancylostoma duodenale*, the European hookworm. The American worm was smaller and formed an S rather than a C curve. The mouth of the European species contained two pairs of teeth, whereas the American worm had no teeth but a pair of shell-like cutting plates. Stiles now looked up Ashford's specimens in the Army Medical Museum and found that these were the same as the Texas worms.

Early in 1902, Stiles reported that he had identified a new kind of American hookworm, found in Texas and Puerto Rico. Whereas his previous interest in hookworms had been purely a sideline, he now was well on his way to becoming the number one American authority on uncinariasis. Ashford, who had identified the disease but not the worm and went on in 1904 to start a successful free clinic for mass treatment of the disease in Puerto Rico, later disputed the priority of his old teacher. His jealousy was understandable; at the time, the importance of his own work was generally over-looked.

Stiles called his hookworm *Uncinaria americanus* or, with an added flourish, *Necator americanus*— "American killer." He regarded *Ancylostoma duode-nale* as the Old World and *Necator americanus* as the New World type. This name, as he later freely ac-knowledged, was a mistake. Within another two or three years, a German, Dr. Arthur Looss (1861-1923), para-sitologist at the government medical school in Cairo, identified *Necator americanus* in pygmies from cen-tral Africa who were on exhibition in a music hall in Alexandria, Egypt.

"This new premise," Stiles wrote, "justified a new deduction, namely, that . . . the presence of this para-site in America is . . . an inheritance of the slave trade . . ."

One other discovery had just taken place that ap-peared to clinch the case. While Stiles was in Germany and Ashford was in Puerto Rico, Dr. Looss solved the mystery of how the disease was transmitted. He acci-dentally spilled a hookworm culture on his hands and developed an itch and tiny sores. When he later found hookworm eggs in his feces, he concluded that he had been infected *through the skin*. He demonstrated that the larva moves from the water film in the soil to the water film on the skin. The warmth of the skin stimu-lates a reaction called thigmotropism (touch-turning), the corkscrew action mentioned earlier. It took a few years for Looss's discovery to sink in. When it did, it revolutionized methods of control. Now the peril of soil pollution and of going barefoot or wearing leaky, wet shoes was recognized.

Most important of all, the worm and its blood disease were now linked with one of the most common of all complaints in the American South—"ground itch," or as some back-country people called it, "dew pizen."

It still remained to be proved that hookworm infection was widespread through the South. Stiles found one person who was willing to listen to him: Surgeon General Walter Wyman (1848-1911) of the United States Public Health and Marine Hospital Service, the forerunner of the present Public Health Service. Wyman made Stiles professor of zoology in the Hygienic Laboratory of the Public Health Service in 1902. Stiles took a trip through the South with a microscope in his bag. All he asked of anyone he met was a sample of his bowel movement! In five hundred miles of travel through the cities and clay lands extending south from Washington, he at first found nothing convincing. Searching his memory of the literature, he recalled occasional mentions that the larvae were found in sandy soil.

Hearing that the land near the Haile gold mines in South Carolina was mainly a granite sand, he went there and found a family of eleven members, all of them infected with hookworms and one an alleged dirt-eater. Seeking the largest plantation in this area, he examined twenty white field hands. All had hookworm disease. The plantation owner told Stiles not to waste time, his other forty men were all in the same condition. Continuing his trip, Stiles found more cases in Georgia and northern Florida.

On his way back to Washington, Stiles pondered the significance of what he had found and, as so often happens in moments of discovery, he could not sleep for three nights. Hoping to attract public attention and stir Congress to action, Stiles rushed a preliminary report

into print. In a government health bulletin, he said:
"There is . . . not the slightest room for doubt that
uncinariasis is one of the most important . . . diseases
of . . . the South, especially on farms and plantations
in sandy districts, and . . . that much of the trouble
popularly attributed to 'dirt-eating' . . . and even some
of the proverbial laziness of the poorer classes of the
white population are . . . manifestations of uncinariasis."

Stiles's report created little public or professional
excitement. His next opportunity to tell his story was
at the meeting of the Sanitary Conference of the Repub-
lics in Washington on December 4, 1902. This time he
was favored with one of the most spectacular pieces of
publicity in the history of American health education,
all of it quite unplanned. A plump, round-faced young
man sat in the front row, just below the speaker's platform; he kept drowsing off and arousing himself during
Stiles's speech, a distraction to the doctor. Suddenly, the
young man began scribbling rapidly. Stiles had just in-
dicted hookworm disease as the probable cause of the
Southern poor whites' well-known lack of energy. The
next morning the New York *Sun* carried the news that
Stiles wanted the United States to hear, under the head-
line: GERM OF LAZINESS FOUND?

The *Sun*'s dispatch was picked up by newspapers
everywhere. Some of the newspaper treatment was serious, but much was facetious. Cartoonists, columnists,
and newspaper poets seized on the "laziness germ" and,
pursuing their own instincts for the sensational twist,
gave the laziness germ a spin equal to its own instinct for
thigmotropism. Mocked *Truth*, in London:

I for long had believed that, concerning my case,
    There existed much popular haziness;

I for years had felt sure it was grossly unfair
    To regard as a failing my laziness;
Now the truth has come out, thanks to good Doctor Stiles,
    And 'tis proved how unjust a strong bias is,
For I, if you please, for my idleness scorned,
    Have been suffering from uncinariasis!

Stiles now had the attention he wanted but it produced more laughter than alarm. Meanwhile Southerners were resentful of all this fun at their expense. Nevertheless, Surgeon General Wyman agreed that a hookworm campaign should be undertaken and assigned Stiles to talk to medical society meetings.

For the next eight years the zoologist was a solitary crusader against hookworm infection. In medical meetings and clinics throughout the South, he advised "20 percent thymol and Epsom salts (treatment) combined with 80 percent sanitation (prevention)." Wherever he went, he carried a kit of thymol and Epsom salts, the first to kill the worms and the second to purge the drug.

Rural people eyed Stiles with suspicion, and more than once a hillbilly waved him on his way with a shotgun. Stiles learned how to react when a gun was pointed at him. He stood still, smiled, and said, "Now, my friend, let's talk this over." Always he ran a risk of offending people's modesty; once a sheriff said he would have to give Stiles a bodyguard, his speech had caused so much public indignation.

For the most part, Southern doctors received him more hospitably, listening to what he had to say, peering through his microscope. Some few began diagnosing and treating the disease. On the other hand, Stiles's hard-hitting professorialism did not go over with others. A colleague observed: "He alienated the country doctors who should have been his main support by impugning their education and public spirit. He said they usually did more harm than good, and his tone of sarcasm and superiority was especially irritating when it became known that he himself was not a doctor of medicine."

Wyman and Stiles recognized the need to improve sanitation of homes, public schools, and churches. In 1903, a portion of one of the Hygienic Laboratory's bulletins was given over to a discussion of the merits and demerits of sanitary privies. This homely dialogue, to be continued for many years, faltered a bit in its beginning. When Stiles submitted his manuscript, the bulletin's editor returned it with a request that the privy portion be deleted on the grounds that it was undignified, in fact disgusting, and deserved no place in a scientific article. Stiles was just the man to change this view: he argued the objectionable portion back into the article and it was printed as he wrote it. As he said, a sanitary privy providing a safe disposal of excreta from rural homes was the key to prevention of hookworm disease. "In those days," he later recalled, "there was a great popular prejudice in rural districts against privies . . . They were unpleasant places . . . Nature's way of disposing of excreta was to expose it to the rays of the sun or to hide it in the brush."

2

Help for the Poor White

The ballyhoo was not enough. It was obvious to Surgeon General Wyman and Stiles that money was needed to finance an intensive campaign against soil pollution in the rural South. Senator Benjamin ("Pitchfork") Tillman, from South Carolina, introduced a bill in Congress providing the Public Health Service $25,000 to start a campaign for rural sanitation, but it found little support.

Thus, Stiles remained a prophet without honor. His first big chance to get adequate financial support came about in the following way.

Stiles learned from a friend in Washington that a certain wealthy resident wished to contribute two million dollars anonymously to a worthy cause. Stiles suggested that the money would finance a movement to combat hookworm disease; the idea appealed to the millionaire and the donation was all set to be signed. A week before the announcement was due, Stiles happened to be chatting with Walter Hines Page (1855-1918), the publisher, while buying that day's newspaper. It told of the sudden death of the would-be benefactor. Stiles could barely speak. Page thought he was ill. After a while, Stiles told him what had happened. The bequest had not been signed.

However, Stiles had told the story to the right person. Former editor of *Atlantic Monthly*, founder of *The World's Work*, a liberal magazine of the day, and partner in the new publishing house, Doubleday, Page & Company, Page was a North Carolinian interested in regeneration of the South, and one of the country's social action leaders. Page was a member of the five-man Country Life Commission appointed by President Theodore Roosevelt to report to him on "the present condition of country life" and make recommendations. The study, published in 1909, described urgent agricultural problems. It received an unfavorable press in the South, because it was done hastily and also because the Commission accepted the notion that hookworm disease was the main thing wrong with Southern country life and publicized this claim while touring the South. The published report merely mentioned the extensive spread of the hookworm disease in the Gulf-Atlantic states and pointed out that many farmhouses and schoolhouses lacked even the rudiments of sanitation.

It was during the Commission's public hearings in various parts of the country in November and December, 1908—mainly one-day schoolhouse meetings—that Stiles told Page the sad story of his "lost angel."

One morning, while their train was traveling through North Carolina, Stiles happened to be sitting in the smoking car with Page and Henry C. Wallace (father of Henry A. Wallace, Vice President of the United States), editor of the Iowa periodical, *Wallace's Farmer*, and a Commission member. On the platform of a country station where the train stopped, the three men saw a miserable figure. His body seemed small in proportion to his elongated limbs. The joints of his fingers were swollen. His shoulders were hunched and angular, his neck scrawny, his stomach dropsically bulging in contrast to his pathetically emaciated frame. His skin had the greenish-yellow tint of tallow and looked like parchment. His eyes seemed faded and vague, his nose was almost transparent, and his mouth sagged. Everything about him sagged.

The sight was a familiar one to Page, but Wallace, from Iowa, was startled. The conversation, Stiles recalled, ran as follows:

Wallace: What on earth is that?

Page (sadly): That is a so-called poor white.

Wallace: If he represents Southern farm labor, the South is in poor luck.

Stiles: That man is a "dirt-eater." His condition is due to hookworm infection; he can be cured at a cost of about fifty cents for drugs, and in a few weeks' time he can be turned into a useful man.

Page (astonished): Is that really a hookworm case? Can he really be cured? You can make a healthy man out of that wreck? Good God! Stiles, are you in earnest?

Page was fascinated. He now committed himself to help Stiles in his crusade, which from this point on constituted a convergence of two lines of philanthropic interest: *public health*, thus far represented mainly by only one body, that of Stiles, and *public education*, represented by a variety of small and large bodies, best exemplified by the Peabody Fund, the Southern Education Fund, and the General Education Board.

Page spoke to Wallace Buttrick, secretary of the General Education Board, one of the largest Rockefeller philanthropies; the Board had been chartered in 1903 to promote education in the United States without re-

gard to race, sex, or religion. Its first interest was in improving public schooling in the South. The Board began
with the assumption that the obstacle to free education
in the rural South was largely an economic one—the
farmer did not make enough money to pay adequate
school taxes. Still, it saw that money was not the whole
question. There was, for example, a baffling mental and
physical sluggishness among country boys and girls in
the South. There was reason to believe they did not get
enough of the right things to eat. Their families ate
mainly sowbelly, cornmeal, and molasses, with only an
occasional dish of collards or potlicker to stave off pel-
lagra and anemia. But here was a new idea: anemia might
be an important factor in poverty and ignorance, and it
could come not only from malnutrition but from a worm
that preyed on the barefooted children who went behind a bush to evacuate.

At a reception for the Country Life Commission
in Ithaca at the end of the schoolhouse tour, Buttrick singled out Stiles and said: "Walter Page says you know
something which I must know immediately; let us go to
my room." Stiles and Buttrick talked hookworm almost
all night.

Returning to New York, Buttrick repeated Stiles's
story to Frederick T. Gates (1853-1929), president of
the General Education Board. Gates, like Buttrick, was a
former Baptist minister who had elected to seek salva-
tion in secular ways. A sort of worldly architect for the
Almighty, with a heavy mustache, shaggy mane, eagle
beak, thundering voice, and generally fierce demeanor,
he had an expansive imagination and a capacity for catch-
ing fire on "pregnant ideas," as he called them.

Hookworm was one of them. Gates summoned
Stiles to New York for a conference. Stiles came, bring-

ing his specimen case, microscope, drawings, photographs, statistics. Gates listened to the zoologist for about forty minutes and then sent for Starr J. Murphy, Rockefeller's personal legal counsel: "This is the biggest proposition ever put up to the Rockefeller office. Listen to what Dr. Stiles has to say. Now, Doctor, start from the beginning again . . ."

Gates was a little disappointed that Stiles could not tell him how many cases of hookworm there were in the South and how much it would cost to eradicate them. Did he have no plan? The zoologist soon came back with one. He estimated that there were two million cases and the cost of eradication would probably be a half million dollars. They used the word *eradication* freely.

Gates now took the proposition to the John D. Rockefellers, Senior and Junior, telling Stiles he would be called on for a demonstration if needed. It was not needed. "They recognized the high importance of the subject," Gates wrote in his unpublished memoirs, "and committed themselves to the needed funds for a campaign of extermination of the hookworm in the United States."

Worried about Southern sensitivities, Gates next tried the idea on members of the Southern Education Board, meeting at Lake George. Stiles put on his show for them. They were eager to lend support, irrespective of criticism. That night, following the meeting, Stiles heard from Gates the words for which he had been waiting: "The Rockefeller office will support this work."

Some weeks later, Gates gave Stiles a momentary sinking feeling by pursuing an established practice in Rockefeller philanthropies. Gates suggested making a small beginning with fifty thousand dollars. Stiles said that would be a drop in the bucket. Asked to name a sum, he said one million dollars. Gates said that such a sum would be forthcoming only on condition that Stiles resigned from his government job and devoted his entire time to the campaign.

Stiles said he thought he had a better plan and would give him an answer in the morning. After breakfast, Gates asked: "What is your answer?" Stiles handed him a letter of resignation that he had written to Surgeon General Wyman, and asked that he be given forty hours' notice before it was mailed to Washington.

The letter was merely a gambit. It was Stiles's idea that the most important immediate objective was sanitation of the country schools. They had no toilets, inside or outside; the boys went in one direction behind the bushes and the girls went in the other. All were barefoot. The campaign should be headed by an educator, such as James Y. Joyner of North Carolina, the first full-time state superintendent of schools in the South and then engaged in a campaign for tax-supported free schools. Surgeon General Wyman should be asked to select health officers with Southern background to work with State Boards of Health in support of the school sanitation program and in cooperation with physicians on diagnosis and treatment. He, Stiles, should not become involved in administration but should continue to do what he already was doing—talking to medical societies, universities, colleges, schools, and other organizations—as promoter of the faith, so to speak. He should stay with the government. Gates said he would think this over, and then talked about prospective trustees.

The organization meeting was held in the Rockefeller office on October 26, 1909. Gates read the letter of gift signed by the elder Rockefeller. "If you deem it wise to undertake this commission," he said, "I shall be glad to be permitted to work with you to that end and you may call upon me from time to time for such sums as may be needed during the next five years for carrying on an aggressive campaign, up to a total of one million dollars . . ." The letter of acceptance was signed by John D. Rockefeller, Jr., Gates, Stiles, Page, and six others present.

The acceptance letter committed the Commission to "a scientific and popular campaign for eradicating Hookworm Disease." The outlook seemed most encouraging: "This disease can be easily recognized, readily and effectively tested, and by simple and proper sanitary precautions successfully prevented."

The Commission elected Gates as chairman. It was agreed the post of administrative secretary would be offered to Joyner. Stiles would be scientific secretary. Gates wanted him full-time, and Stiles hoped that the Public Health Service would assign him to the Commission for its duration.

The first step meanwhile, it decided, was to announce the gift and creation of the Commission through the Associated Press. The news was the signal for another round of hookworm hullabaloo, reminiscent of 1902. Some newspapers sang the praises of John D. Rockefeller, but the Macon *Telegraph* wanted to know, "Where was this hookworm or lazy disease when it took five Yankee soldiers to whip one Southerner?" Bishop Chandler of Georgia, a longtime critic of Rockefeller and his wealth, led the clerical opposition. He regarded the whole thing as a plot to control Southern education, and said, "The Southern people will not be taken in by Mr. Rockefeller's vermifuge fund."

The day following the organization meeting, Stiles

talked to Surgeon General Wyman about detailing federal public health officers to the hookworm work. Wyman was enthusiastic, but the Treasury Department
under President Taft soon vetoed the proposal, and the
Rockefeller Sanitary Commission from then on had to
improvise.

Gates informed the Commission at its second meeting, in December, of Joyner's refusal of the job of staff
director. Joyner wanted to finish the fight that he had
started for free schools. Gates also had had news from
Stiles. The Secretary of the Treasury would not assign
him to the Commission in such a way as to constitute
government recognition of its mission, but would grant
him a leave of absence for one year.

Buttrick now suggested Wickliffe Rose (1862-
1931), a native Tennesseean, of Nashville, for the number one staff position. Rose was general agent of the
Peabody Fund and executive secretary of the Southern
Education Board. Then forty-seven years old, he had
been a professor of mathematics, philosophy, history, and
of the philosophy of education and later dean of the Peabody College and University of Nashville (a combined
institution) from 1891 to 1907. Another boy who had to
work his way, he had obtained his A.B. degree rather
late, when he was twenty-seven, and received an M.A.
the following year.

Rose was a small, inconspicuous man with a rather
large head and tiny feet. He wore a high collar, bow tie,
and pince-nez glasses on a black ribbon, and spoke in a
precise manner, with only a slight Southern accent. He
admitted to close friends that he felt a fascination for the
unknown—always, he said, he wanted to know what
was around the corner. Rose's associates often remarked

the clarity with which he articulated his thoughts; when he finished speaking at a board meeting, there never seemed to be anything more to be said.

Rose's first inclination was to decline. He had just been offered the presidency of Peabody College. Furthermore, what did he know about public health and medical science? But he was an educator and a Southerner, and did have this spirit of adventure and an Aristotelian disposition to learn by doing.

One wakeful night, during a Southern Education Board conference at Lake George, he came to a decision. With characteristic enthusiasm, he at once sat down to outline an attack on hookworm disease in the American South, formulating principles of operation that would serve not only the Rockefeller Sanitary Commission but the Rockefeller Foundation to come. How much Wickliffe Rose could foresee at this moment is unrecorded, Rose never having been enough of an egotist to write his memoirs, but he had elected to lead the first entry of private philanthropy into the field of public health. Though not a physician himself, he would in the next thirteen years become one of the greatest, though least-known figures in American public health.

The Commission on January 15, 1910, appointed Rose as its administrative secretary at a salary of $7,500 a year. He opened headquarters in the Union Trust Building in Washington, D.C., a three-room suite leased for $85 a month. Stiles continued to maintain his office at the Hygienic Laboratory at 24th and E streets, Northwest. The neutral territory of the national capital, Gates explained, was chosen on the assumption that New York was too far north of the Mason-Dixon Line to please Southerners. At its next meeting, on February 3, the Rockefeller Sanitary Commission for the Eradication of

Hookworm Disease adopted its name and articles of incorporation, and made Rose a member of the Commission. This unique organization was now fully formed. It consisted of two professional philanthropists, one attorney, one zoologist, two physicians, one editor, and six educators.

Rose outlined the plan for the organization and operation of the Commission. The Rockefeller Commission has been organized to eradicate hookworm disease. To accomplish this end it would be necessary to do three things. These were (1) to locate the areas of infection and determine the degree of infection in each area, (2) to organize "a relief corps" to cure infected persons, and (3) to remove the cause of infection by establishing a system of sanitation.

In the organization of state programs, Rose said that he would select a physician to become the administrative head of the Commission's work in each state: "Preferably this man will be young, energetic, forceful; he will possess good judgment, executive ability, the qualities of leadership; he will be familiar with laboratory practice and will have a clinical experience with the diseases involved in the problem of public health; he will be able to command the respect of the medical profession and the confidence of the people of the state; he will prefer the public health service to private practice and will desire to devote his life to the work." The Commission would pay this man's salary and travel expenses on condition he be appointed by the state board of health and that he work under the general direction of the state department of health and of the Commission. This man would have the services of the state laboratory or, if it lacked one, a laboratory in a nearby medical school. He would seek to locate and report every case of hookworm disease in the state; for this investigation of incidence, the county would be the working unit. The state director would have a corps of inspectors for field work.

The "relief corps" would consist of practicing physicians of the state, especially country doctors who knew how to diagnose and treat the disease. The corps would be organized in three ways: 1. The state director of hookworm work would hold a one-week clinic at his laboratory for doctors, picked one from each county, the doctors' expenses to be paid. Each would return to his own county and hold a one-week clinic, to which all physicians would be invited on an expenses-paid basis. 2. Every physician would receive detailed instructions in printed form. 3. The state director would give demonstrations from time to time at convenient places and would attend regular meetings of county medical societies. In addition, medical schools would be encouraged to give proper instruction to future doctors.

The last stage would be "putting in operation a system of sanitation," something "which will require a long period of time and the cooperation of a large number of agencies." The methods here would be investigation and publication of the facts needed to make the public conscious of the necessity for action. The campaign would be carried on through speeches, circulars, pamphlets, and the daily press. The aid of charitable organizations, women's clubs, school improvement leagues, ministers, teachers, and practicing physicians would be enlisted. Private and public schools and colleges would be asked to instruct their students in personal sanitation. Schools would be used as a means of reaching into the homes of the community—that is, parents would be reached through their children. In due course, the Commission would seek public health legislation in each state to enforce proper sanitation and to stimulate larger expenditures for public health.

Here was a philanthropic philosophy of helping people to help themselves. The new secretary, in his first annual report, said that the eradication of this disease was a work that no outside agency, working independently, could do for a people even if it would, and one which no outside agency should do if it could. The states in which the disease exists must assume the responsibility. An outside agency can be helpful only insofar as it aids the states in organizing and bringing into activity their own forces. In any case, Rose emphasized, the first step toward action was for a state health department to invite the Rockefeller Sanitary Commission's cooperation. Without such an invitation the Commission could not take action. This step was important, though it was to some extent a formality, for the initiative lay with the Commission. On the other hand, Rose was so convinced of the necessity of self-effacement that he declined to give newspaper interviews and urged state officials not to call attention to the Commission. As a result, local newspaper accounts of the campaign as it progressed in each area usually contained only the briefest mention of the sanitary commission.

Since Rose was unknown in medical and public health circles, some associates advised him to work through the state boards of education. He rejected the idea and chose state health officers, on the theory that if the state had no health department, this approach might help create one; if it had a weak department, this would strengthen it. Beginning in January, Rose traveled from state to state in his quest for staff doctors and then, as his first approach to the medical profession, attended a meeting in Atlanta of outstanding physicians and public health officials from the twelve hookworm states. Some three hundred were at the meeting, and Rose talked to many of them. He was so reasonable, so modest, that the doctors liked him; indeed, there is no record of a word of medical disrespect for this layman from that time on.

The first state director of sanitation (the title varied) was appointed in February—Dr. Allen W. Freeman (1881-1954), who was placed in charge of hookworm disease control in Virginia. The second was in March—Dr. John A. Ferrell (1880-1965), in North Carolina.

By November 1910, programs had been undertaken in nine states—Virginia, North Carolina, Georgia, South Carolina, Tennessee, Arkansas, Mississippi, Alabama, and Louisiana (Texas and Kentucky joined later; Florida declined). Each director organized a force of sanitary inspectors who were physicians; they undertook health education in the schools, examined and treated patients in demonstration clinics, and sought the cooperation of community leaders.

The field staff numbered more than forty by the end of 1910. Each field man was equipped with a microscope (a folding one that, if necessary, could be stuffed in a saddlebag). Each carried drugs, literature, slides, and a projector. Each also had a camera and took his own photographs of local cases to illustrate lectures and reports and, as one said, "to make the story so simple, so direct, so vivid that every child will feel it tingle on the bottom of his bare foot when he walks on polluted soil."

The salaries offered did not violate the Rockefeller policy of frugality in compensation of employees: $2,500 a year plus $800 for expenses, for a state director of sanitation; and $1,200 to $1,800 plus $400 expenses, for a san-

itary inspector, or field worker. Eventually a ceiling of
$1,000 a year was established for expenses of field work-
ers. After all, it cost as much as $2 a day to rent a horse
and buggy or a saddle horse to carry one beyond the
railroad depot.

3

The Campaign

It was easy to demonstrate, through microscopic examination of fecal specimens, that hookworm infection was prevalent in the South to a degree that few doctors believed until they saw or heard the evidence.

People were not all so easily won. One oldster came in for specimen tins but had little use for the goings-on. The doctor tried to interest him by showing him a fly's foot under the microscope.

"Thet ain't no fly's foot. Thet's a June bug."

"All right," said the doctor. "You catch a fly for me and we'll put that one under the microscope."

The old man caught a fly. After looking at it for some time from every angle, he started to walk away without comment.

"Well, what do you think of your fly now?" the doctor called.

The old man pushed his hat to the opposite side of his head, and squinted at the doctor.

"I don't believe whut y'said—and I don't believe whut I seen neither."

There were many variations in the details of treatment with thymol and Epsom salts. The so-called standard routine was as follows:

First day: 6 or 8 P.M. Epsom salts.

Second day: 6 A.M. Two capsules of thymol (usually twenty grains per capsule); 8 A.M. Two capsules of thymol, no breakfast; 10 A.M. Epsom salts; Noon. Light lunch.

The idea of the first purge was to clean out the intestine so the drug would reach all the worms. The second purge was to expel the dead worms. Inasmuch as thymol has a peculiar odor and a burning taste, it was necessary to swallow it in a dissolvable capsule.

The drug is poisonous if taken at full strength in large quantities. With the anti-hookworm dosage, fatalities were rare. Thomas Taylor and his three sons were found infected and took the treatment home. The next morning, after they had the thymol, Thomas, Jr., and Timothy went to play in the barn. When they came into the house, they were given the final dose of salts. They immediately vomited, Thomas vomiting blood. The doctor was called and when he arrived both boys were paralyzed. By the next morning, both were dead. Whether the boys had eaten something harmful while outside could not be established. The father and third son, Daniel, were unaffected. One child with a previous sensitivity to thymol died of drug poisoning; her parents did not mention that thymol had made her sick before. But these were unusual events among the tens of thousands receiving treatment.

Stiles presented something of a special case, his role being defined as advisory to the Commission and as scientific spokesman to the medical profession. Continuing to maintain his base in the Hygienic Laboratory of the Public Health Service, he showed no particular interest in financial reward and accepted $2,500 a year plus travel and laboratory expenses. He continued to do much more of the same work he had done for the past eight years. In the first year, he addressed 122 meetings and clinics and wrote 31 papers.

Stiles provided the Commission's Publication No. 1, "Soil Pollution as Cause of Ground-Itch, Hookworm Disease (Ground-Itch Anemia), and Dirt-Eating," a twenty-seven-page circular for use in schools. Pupils were advised to take it home and read it to their parents.

To the teachers, Stiles pointed out that an epidemic of yellow fever, cholera, or bubonic plague causes great public excitement but that there was a much greater loss of life from diseases constantly with us, such as tuberculosis and typhoid fever. He apologized that although health education would enable them, personally, to save human life, it involved subjects ordinarily not mentioned in the schoolroom before boys and girls.

After describing hookworm disease, Stiles asked some pertinent questions along these lines: "Is there a privy in your yard? Is there a privy at your school? Is there a privy at your church? How should a privy be built?"

Stiles knew the answers. From his survey in 1910 of nearly 5,000 farm homes in six Southern states, he found 35 percent of the white and 77 percent of the Negro homes had no privy of any kind. Rural schools and churches were worse. Virtually none had a privy.

Stiles was explicit in his directions for the construction of a sanitary privy: "There should be a pail, or a barrel, or a tub, or a watertight box under the seat and the privy should be closed in back so that chickens, hogs, and dogs cannot reach the discharges. Further, the tub should contain a disinfectant such as cresol or a cupful of crude oil or kerosene in water to keep flies away. The privy should be cleaned once or twice a week, with a fresh layer of sand or dirt in the tub. The discharges should be buried two feet deep, down hill from and certainly not nearer than 300 feet to any well or spring. Or burned. Or put in a pit protected from flies and permitted to ferment."

This was asking a great deal of people accustomed to pursuing "nature's way" out in "the handy woods." But Stiles was a zealot in his crusade, and yet he apparently had no illusion about the speed with which the Commission could introduce the sanitary privy as an institution of rural life. Human nature being what it is, he thought it might take at least one and perhaps as many as five generations to eradicate hookworm disease. Treatment could cure many individuals, and thereby save their health at the time, but it could never stay ahead of new infections and reinfections as long as daily exposure to polluted soil prevailed.

Dr. Hiram Byrd, Florida's assistant state health officer, sounded a gloomy warning in 1910, not long after Mr. Rose had visited Florida to study the hookworm disease control program that state had begun in 1909. Florida was more generously endowed with public health funds than other Southern states, having established a half-mill tax to create a special fund for maintenance of the State Board of Health. The tax then yielded $75,000 a year, several times more than what was available in the other states; some, such as Arkansas, did not even have a state health department. Rose received courteous treatment in Florida, but the state stayed out of the program. Dr. Byrd was apparently disturbed by this layman's enthusiasm and optimism.

He said, "So far as the State Board of Health of

Florida is concerned, it has practically abandoned the term 'eradication of hookworm,' and for the present, at least, looks only to ameliorating it . . ."

At issue was how one can exert leadership and still strike a happy balance between pessimism and optimism, between the real and the ideal. Can one arouse the public to make an effort to solve a social problem without running the risk of overstating the possibilities for solution?

Rose took the trouble to go to Puerto Rico in 1910 to study the work of the Puerto Rico Anemia Commission, formed in 1904 by Dr. Bailey K. Ashford. Ashford and two other physicians constituted the Commission. They started a free clinic at Bayamon in an army tent and, with the encouragement of the sugar and coffee growers, expanded their program of free diagnosis and treatment to cover the entire island by holding clinics at fifty-nine different places. This was the first organized attack on hookworm disease anywhere, and Ashford was justly proud of its accomplishment in sharply reducing the anemia death rate in Puerto Rico. He became aggrieved, as the time went on, that his pioneer work was lost from view in the shadows of first Stiles, then the Rockefeller Sanitary Commission, and finally the International Health Division.

Rose in his first annual report saw the tasks of each state health department as teaching the people by demonstration . . . by examinations made at the State laboratory . . . by examination of the school children . . . by example . . . by means of public lectures and the printed page. In the beginning he believed that the country doctor in private practice would be the backbone of the program. Sanitation was the ultimate goal and health education was the only means of achieving it on a mass basis. In teaching, example is better than precept. Here is where the doctor came in. Diagnosis and treatment were tangible and almost immediate in their results. You could show a patient his hookworm eggs under the microscope and he could see the expelled hookworms with his naked eye. When cured, he felt better and his friends and relatives could see that he looked better. The educator saw the physician as the protagonist in a fight against disease.

The task was to enlist the cooperation of nearly 20,000 physicians covering 416,000 square miles of territory in nine states.

But, even as Rose discussed it so simply and clearly, the answer to who would pay for the treatment of the indigent—and the bulk of hookworm patients were indigent—remained one of the most stubborn practical problems. Florida, with its magnificent $75,000 annual public health fund, was offering private physicians three dollars for each indigent patient cured. Other states could not afford this kind of money. Many North Carolina and Virginia doctors agreed to treat the poor free, and some voluntary organizations set out to raise funds to pay for thymol and Epsom salts. Some cotton mill owners absorbed the drug expense.

Over all, the immediate response of private physicians was not encouraging, even taking account of the many public-spirited doctors and the alert, conscientious, and hardworking clinicians interested in advances in medical knowledge and eager to give their patients the benefit of each advance. It wasn't only a question of the fee, for in Florida physicians treated only 602 indigent cases in 1910. Even that year, largely one of organizing and getting under way, the nine states cooperating in the program did better, their physicians treating 8,000 or an average of nearly 900 per state.

Rose, with the encouragement of Stiles, in 1911 changed his mind about relying on the country doctor. He had come back from Puerto Rico opposed to the idea of free clinics, believing that Americans would not come to them. But Dr. Waller S. Leathers (1874-1946), director of public health in Mississippi, suggested it as a solution of the mass treatment problem. Columbia, Mississippi, had started a free dispensary for the treatment of hookworm disease in Marion County. The county board of supervisors appropriated funds to buy drugs. The county health officer provided four rooms and a lavatory. The Commercial Club of Columbia furnished the rooms with beds. The local doctors offered to give the treatments. The dispensary was soon running at full capacity and turning away hundreds.

The inspiration for the dispensary had been Stiles. In 1903, Dr. Charles C. Bass, a Tulane graduate who had just started a rural practice in Columbia, heard Stiles speak in New Orleans about *Necator americanus.* Bass examined the worms under the microscope and took a look at the exhibits of anemia—the pot-bellied sufferers of hookworm disease. "My God," he said, "that's what's the matter with the children in Columbia." He bought a microscope and took it home with him, where he related Stiles's story to his associate in practice, Dr. Hector H. Howard (1873-1960). They soon discovered that hookworm was the principal disease in their community and began treating it forthwith. Columbia therefore had been preconditioned for the dispensary opened there in December 1910, by Dr. C. J. Cully of Leathers' staff.

The idea that struck Rose was that the clinic in Columbia—he called it a county dispensary—could serve as an educational center. Although he did not say so, such an emphasis might relieve the Commission of some of the burden of responsibility it had so confidently accepted. The object would be free treatment as a *demonstration* rather than as *eradication* of all hookworm disease. The Columbia dispensary began in a fixed place, but its countywide status could be implemented by emulating the mobile clinics in the Puerto Rican program, essentially a team of doctors moving from one appointed place to another. The notion of a one-week county clinic conducted by private practitioners was now abandoned in favor of a county dispensary open one day a week over a period of six to eight weeks, and conducted by the field staff with the cooperation of county officials and local doctors. Usually, the dispensary was held in five different places in a given county. Rose noted that demonstrations in one county stimulated the interest of adjoining counties, and had the effect of inducing many persons to go to their own doctors for treatment.

Accepting Mississippi's lead, Alabama and North Carolina soon followed suit, with six other states adopting the dispensary program in 1911. Kentucky became the tenth in 1911 and Texas brought the total to eleven in 1912.

The anti-hookworm crusade now had the combined characteristics of a medicine show, revival, and picnic. The general procedure was to obtain a token appropriation from the county commission, try to enlist the support of the county medical society, and then to advertise the coming clinic through newspapers, posters, and lectures.

People came from twenty to thirty miles around, by wagon, boat, train. Men, women, and children walked ten or twelve miles, the more anemic dropping by the road until a passing wagon gave them a lift.

The numbers attending a one-day clinic ran as high as 450. The hookworm doctor would lecture from time to time and show his charts and worms. The people would start arriving before 8 A.M. and stay most of the day, listening, looking, singing hymns, eating their lunches, and making up their minds about being examined. There was usually the joker with the bandaged hand, where the worms had bitten him, and the rumors of someone in the next county who had been poisoned to death by the treatment. Examinations and treatments were continued during the subsequent weekly sessions until the law of diminishing returns set in. Then the clinic moved on.

4

"Greatest Thing That Ever Come"

At its peak in 1914 the hookworm program employed 183 workers, ninety-nine of them physicians and the rest laymen. In five years, 1910-1914, nearly 1.3 million persons were examined for hookworm infection and nearly 700,000 were treated. This was the tangible accomplishment of the campaign.

The figures would indicate that more than half of those examined had either hookworm infection (carried the worms) or hookworm disease (anemia and other symptoms). But to conclude that every other Southerner had hookworm would be to misinterpret a sample preselected for suspicion of exposure to hookworm infection. The best index to the prevalence of hookworm infection in the South came from five years of microscopic examinations of stool specimens from more than a half million children in eleven states. Thirty-nine percent were found to be infected, with a variation from one county to another of 2.5 to 94 percent.

The Rockefeller Sanitary Commission was systematic and kept copious records, but its statistical methods were not sufficiently refined and controlled to measure progress. In human as opposed to statistical terms, however, the story was a powerful one. The reports of the field staff and of the Commission itself were filled with exhibits of before-and-after photographs and doctor-and-patient testimonials to the wonders of thymol. One case was entitled, "A Father Sees the Treatment of His Own Son in Terms of Dollars and Cents." The father brought his fifteen-year-old son to the dispensary in Chadbourn, North Carolina, after seeing the pamphlets and leaflets. The boy was cadaverous-looking and submitted to the examination "with the most profound indifference," and then, too tired to stand, immediately went and sat on a nearby log. The father was instructed to bring the boy back for a second treatment. The father came back alone to the next dispensary, much excited. He said that before the boy had always been of no account, worthless, trifling. He would lie on the porch like a dog and yet it had been hard to believe he was sick, for when the dinner bell rang he was the first at the table and the last to leave and ate more than a farm hand. And now, "Aside from saving my boy," the father told the doctor, "this thing means money in my pocket. Before I saw you I had to feed and clothe him and care for him at a dead expense. . . . I had to hire a man to take the work I counted on his doing. When I left home, that boy was following a plow and yelling at the mule in a way to let you know that he was just glad to be living!"

Della Carder of Grant County, Arkansas, was pictured as skin and bones at sixteen and a bright-looking healthy girl after treatment for hookworm. She had been almost an invalid since childhood, and thought to have malaria and tuberculosis. As usual in post-puberty cases such as hers, the girl began to menstruate only after getting rid of the parasites.

A common exhibit was of an infected and runty boy photographed beside his uninfected and much larger brother who was several years younger. A special example was Herrod Moore, eighteen, of Heber Springs, Arkansas. Nicknamed "Chalky" for his pallor, he weighed eighty-two pounds. Photographed with him was his nephew, two months younger but fifty pounds heavier. Dr. J. M. Flippin of Mt. Airy, North Carolina, reported that one fourteen-year-old boy gained thirty pounds in weight and two inches in height in six months after being relieved of his worms. One hundred percent families and 100 percent schoolrooms—100 percent infected— were also favorites. The Rogers family in Lawrence County, Mississippi, held a record: seventeen members, all infected.

The 1913 annual report pictured Joseph Fowler of Cocke County, Tennessee, who had set some kind of record in the characteristic perverted appetite of hookworm disease. He "has eaten one whole Bible and almost all of a second one." And there were stories of grinding poverty arising from quackery on the one hand and medical ignorance on the other—the hookworm-infected Tennessee family which spent $1,500 on patent medicines, and the Mississippi mother who sold her last horse and cow to buy her family medicines for the wrong diseases.

In his many field visits, Rose found communities where hookworm disease kept a large proportion of the children out of school. He was particularly impressed with the work of Dr. A. C. Fisher of Emmerton, in the Northern Neck section of Virginia. Northern Neck lies between the Rappahannock and Potomac rivers, extending through four counties. Dr. Fisher found an average infection rate of 82.6 percent in the school children he examined in Richmond County, the problem being particularly severe among the "Forkemites," people who lived in the vicinity of a wide-spreading fork in a tidewater creek and who for generations were known for their lack of energy, extreme poverty, and low mental and moral state. Of the forty Forkemite children in the Totus Key school, thirty-eight were infected. These were a minor problem—there were forty-five children with much severer infections who had never gone to school. At the school, Rose took pleasure in inspecting two sanitary privies, just built. He also met Willie King, twenty-six years old, working in the fields. A year before, King had been given up to die, with chronic ulcers eating away his legs. Now, thanks to Dr. Fisher, he was "feelin' fine," newly married, and making a corn crop.

Rose talked to families which had staggered along with their burden of hookworms, now and then digging a grave for a member who could no longer carry his load. There was Mrs. Sydnor, for instance, who told of losing two children to anemia and having four others ill. They couldn't work or go to school. Now all except the youngest, who needed more treatment, were "doin' fine." Wrote Rose, in a long letter to Gates about this trip: "And as the old mother came to the end of her story and tried to express her gratitude, she faltered, then referred to what is being done also for others; and raising her hand she said, 'It is the greatest thing that ever come.' "

In the running argument between Stiles and Ferrell on what kind of privy they should settle for, Rose was inclined to the pit privy—any kind of an outhouse that would keep out flies and rainwater and was built over a seat with a deep hole beneath. He agreed that the pit privy presented some danger of water pollution in swampy areas where the drinking water was pumped from shallow wells and in limestone regions where polluted fluids may run off for some distance through crevices. On the other hand, a pit privy that was flyproof and placed a considerable distance from the water supply probably represented the highest type of sanitation that some localities would be able to develop for years to come. Unfortunately, it was not good enough.

Rose wanted to put the idea of eradication to the ultimate test. An intensive community program was attempted, beginning in September 1913, on Knotts Island, a remote fishing village on the North Carolina coast with little contact with the mainland. The plan was to treat and sanitate until the job was done. Ninety-four of the 567 inhabitants had hookworm and ninety were cured by Christmas. Four stubborn old persons would have nothing to do with this business of stool specimens, thymol, and Epsom salts. The sanitation program was less successful. There was no really attractive solution to the rural latrine problem except installation of septic tanks, and this was too expensive.

Total eradication was not achieved on Knotts Island; nor when the Commission extended this wring-out approach to twelve communities in Virginia, North Carolina, South Carolina, and Louisiana during 1914.

The cost of the five-year campaign was $797,888.36 to Rockefeller and $90,366.46 in county appropriations. This made the cost per treated case $1.15 to Rockefeller and 13 cents to the counties.

Gates and Rose brought the Sanitary Commission program to a close at the end of 1914. While one of the earliest, it was not the first of these typically American public crusades against disease. There were some precedents in the voluntary educational campaign against tuberculosis and the official public health attack on ty-phoid fever. But the anti-hookworm crusade did lay down a pattern of cooperation between voluntary and official health agencies that was original.

Some lessons were learned (some have had to be relearned many times since). The campaign thoroughly demonstrated that hookworm disease was in many cases curable and, to the extent that rural people could be persuaded to change custom, preventable. Many physicians had taken part in the program, yet on the whole practicing doctors themselves proved difficult to move; only about 30 percent of the physicians of the eleven Southern states ultimately reported that they were treating the disease.

The state and county superintendents of schools and the teachers themselves for the most part demonstrated a readiness to instruct children in the dangers of soil pollution as a regular part of their education. Rose described the teachers as the most effective allies. It became evident, of course, that instruction would have to be a continuous process until the children grew up and replaced the not-so-educable adults.

The press showed itself to be an accurate mirror of popular opinion and civic leadership. Whereas in 1909 various newspapers had kidded about the germ of laziness and the hookworm fad, or refused to believe the disease existed at all, not one instance of unfriendliness or noncooperation could be noted in 1914. Southern newspapers were considered to be behind the campaign 100 percent.

Laws requiring the use of sanitary privies at all public schools were enacted and enforced in Virginia and Louisiana. In North Carolina, the state department of education would not accept a new schoolhouse from the contractor until it was provided with sanitary privies. In several states, county boards of education assumed responsibility for building sanitary privies at their schoolhouses.

There had been a variety of miscalculations that required a little rationalization in the end. There was an overestimate of the literal promise of eradication— no matter whose responsibility it actually was. All-important as education is, Rose perhaps had placed too much confidence in its ability to change human attitudes rapidly. And Stiles had underestimated the number of hookworm infections to be controlled. Instead of the 2,000,000 cases he had estimated in the beginning, the figure was more in the order of 3,000,000 to 4,000,000 at the end. Also, he had misjudged the extent of resistance to the bucket privy. Human nature was on the side of the hookworm.

5

"Henceforth . . . the World"

The enthusiasm of Frederick Gates, it can be said in retrospect, was only exceeded by the innocence of Wickliffe Rose. In a letter he wrote to the elder Rockefeller at the time, Gates called up some useful rhetoric from his early days as a preacher: "So I say to Dr. Rose, 'Well done, good and faithful servant. Thou hast been faithful over a few things; we will make thee ruler over many things. Henceforth, thy field is the world . . .'" Lewis Hackett, on the other hand, later summed up the transition that now took place with the typical hardihood of a public health officer: "Mr. Rose was no tenderfoot when he entered the field of international health. The International Health Commission was first seeded and strengthened in the soil of the South before it was transplanted overseas . . ."

There is nothing of record, however, to show that either Gates or Rose was a student of international relations prior to 1913, or that they planned the I.H.C. as a new means of overcoming existing obstacles to international cooperation. For more than sixty years, governments had debated their common health problems and were still unable to agree on concerted action against a single disease, even though medical science had opened up avenues of attack.

Some half dozen International Sanitary Conventions were held from 1851 to 1907, but the great powers were unable to agree on anything except that they should report epidemics and enforce port quarantines against the pestilential diseases that traveled the world's trade routes. These were smallpox, plague, typhus, cholera, and yellow fever. All left gruesome trails of death and misery, and all seemed in their origin to identify with foreigners. The ancient guiding principle of international health still prevailed: *noli me tangere*—touch me not. There was no special interest on either side of international boundaries in such everyday killers as tuberculosis, malaria, dysentery, pneumonia, and typhoid fever. Hookworm disease had been beneath notice.

The fundamental problem in these early international health efforts was that, out of national pride, ignorance, and distrust of the foreigner, no sovereign state was willing to surrender any of its power. What would the people say of any politician so unpatriotic as to give away any element of a country's right of self-determination? Nobody went so far as to find out.

Now came the Rockefeller Foundation, a new organization, a private one, without advance preparation or consultation, with no foreign experience, and with only incomplete knowledge of its task, with a proposal to cross frontiers and establish a front against disease on foreign soil. The younger Rockefeller asked Rose to draw up a plan for a world campaign against hookworm disease. The trustees were already aware there was a problem. In 1911, Gates, looking ahead, had asked Rose to make a world hookworm survey. Rose did it by letter, with the aid of Surgeon General Wyman, who enlisted the assistance of the Department of State in making an official inquiry through its diplomatic officers in foreign countries. This request for information was followed up by correspondence with physicians and public health authorities as well as by a search of the literature in the Surgeon General's library.

It was this survey that fixed the 66° hookworm belt around the earth's middle. Forty-six countries within this tropical and subtropical zone reported general and widespread infection, with as many as nine out of ten persons infected in some areas.

British Guiana reported a 50 percent infection rate for the total population, with near-saturation rates among sugar plantation workers, most of them coolies imported from India. A doctor in Antigua asserted that hookworm disease was "sapping the life and energy of the population." One in Ecuador said that on the Babahoyo cocoa plantations the anemias of hookworm and chronic malaria reduced the work output 67 percent. Wherever one looked—on cocoa, coffee, sugar, rubber, tobacco, or banana plantations—hookworm disease appeared to be a staple by-product.

India, with 60 to 80 percent of its 300 million population infected, presented a massive problem not only to itself but to the many tropical countries, such as British and Dutch Guiana, Ceylon, the Federated Malay States, the Straits Settlement, and Java, that imported Tamil and other Indian coolies as farm laborers and with them a heavy burden of worms and eggs that soon polluted the fresh environment. A doctor in Malaya examined 2,000 sick Tamils employed on a rubber estate and found 100 percent infected; of those still able to work, 60 percent were infected.

The forty-six affected foreign countries, according to Rose's tally, had a population of 919,858,243. Adding twenty million for the eleven Southern states, this meant that about 940,000,000 of the world's population—then 1,600,000,000—lived in hookworm countries. It was easy to imagine there might be from a quarter to a half billion cases of hookworm infection in the world.

Here was a health problem equal to Gates's ambition.

Rose presented his plan at a trustees' meeting in June 1913. Conceptually, he offered nothing new. The Rockefeller Sanitary Commission provided a tested pattern of working through state and local governments to survey, treat, and prevent hookworm infection, and he now simply proposed to do this on an international scale. For this purpose, Rose divided the countries of the hookworm belt into six groups: 1. The United States and possessions; 2. Latin America; 3. British Colonial Empire; 4. French Colonial Empire; 5. Dutch Colonial Empire; 6. the Far East.

According to the map, it appeared that, outside of the old Spanish Main, all of the tropics except Abyssinia and Siam consisted of colonies belonging to one European power or another. Many heavily infected areas were part of the British Empire. There would be two advantages in beginning there: the similarity of language, traditions, and sympathies, at least at the official level, and the fact that Walter H. Page had become United States Ambassador to the Court of St. James. Page could be counted on to pull strings.

The trustees approved the plan and authorized the

executive committee to create an International Health Commission.* This was accomplished on June 27, 1913. Rose was named its director at $10,000 a year. There were twelve members, with John D. Rockefeller, Jr., as chairman.

Gates wrote the resolution creating the new organization. The pivotal declaration was "that this Foundation is prepared to extend to other countries and people the work of eradicating hookworm disease as opportunity offers, and as far as practicable to follow up the treatment and cure of this disease with the establishment of agencies for the promotion of public sanitation and the spread of the knowledge of scientific medicine."

In other words, Gates and Rose regarded demonstrations in the control of hookworm disease as a means to a greater end, government establishment of rural health services, or, as Rose often called it, an entering wedge.

One assumption was clear: this was not a research organization. There was a gap between scientific knowledge and its mass application in the relief and control of hookworm disease. The program was a demonstration in applied science. Dr. Simon Flexner (1863-1946), director of the Rockefeller Institute for Medical Research, was a trustee of the Foundation and member of the new Commission. Gates and Rose agreed with Flexner that medical research was the province of the Institute. If work in the field turned up questions that demanded laboratory answers, the Institute or perhaps a university would help out with the necessary research.

* The Commission was renamed the International Health Board in 1916 and made the International Health Division of the Foundation in 1927. To avoid confusion, we shall call it Division, or I.H.D., throughout.

6

First Demonstration Overseas

From this point on, the story of Wickliffe Rose, first salesman of world health, reads like a travelogue combining meetings of dignitaries in the highest and most fashionable places of civilization and staff assignments to some of the farthest and lowliest places, where it was not uncommon to find primitive people dwelling in ugliness and filth, in some instances defecating in the water which they used for drinking and washing.

Rose's first step was to write Ambassador Page in London. Should he come over there to enlist the cooperation of English scientists, physicians, and government officials? In July 1913, Page cabled Rose in Washington: "Everything ready. Come."

David F. Houston, now Secretary of Agriculture, endeavored to interest President Woodrow Wilson, inaugurated earlier that year, and William Jennings Bryan, Secretary of State, in hearing Rose's plans and giving him Federal government endorsement. The President was interested but evasive. Rose, impatient of delay, sailed in August, without Wilson's specific blessing.

Great Britain welcomed Rose. He dined with Sir

Thomas Barlow (1845-1945), His Majesty's physician, and 150 other physicians attending a medical meeting, and again at the Marlborough Club with Ambassador Page and his guests, who included Lewis Harcourt, Secretary of State for the Colonies, and Lord Crewe, Secretary of State for India, as well as others in the British colonial administrative and medical services. They heard his story, understood it, and supplemented it from their own knowledge. Dr. Fleming M. Sandwith, (1853-1918), who had cooperated with Looss in Egypt in his study of the hookworm's life cycle, was there and spoke for British medical officials when he told Rose: "You have got much further in one evening than we have been able to go altogether."

Harcourt extended an "urgent invitation" to the International Health Division to visit the British colonies with the backing of his Colonial Office. It was agreed that the first point of attack would be in the British West Indies and after that Egypt, Ceylon, and the Malay States, leaving the toughest and most complex of them all, India, until the Commission had more experience.

On the morning of October 4 Rose reported to the trustees in New York on his London trip and that afternoon sailed for the Barbados, Antigua, St. Lucia, St. Vincent, Grenada, Trinidad, and British Guiana, it being understood that later he would go to Egypt and Ceylon (which he did in 1914).

He chose British Guiana, on the northeast coast of South America, for the first demonstration, pursuing his policy of taking the easy ones first. This hot, dreary, damp colony, with most of its population living in mud-flat villages at sea level, had been struggling with the problems of hookworm and malaria since 1907. The sugar plantation managers, under pressure from the Colonial Office to provide sanitary conditions for their immigrant workers, had in most instances installed latrines and indoctrinated the coolies in their use. The swamp people had not been helped, however. They were mainly Negroes, the descendants of slaves who had been freed in 1838 and had chosen to go on living as before in little villages that resembled slave yards, surrounded by rice fields. Among them were some Indian coolies who had worked out their indentures. The houses were of the most primitive sort. There were no springs or wells. The villagers obtained their drinking water from open drainage ditches, where ducks and geese swam, where cattle came to drink, and where the people washed their clothes and bathed. The rain washed the refuse and sewage from the roads and yards into the ditches.

Rose saw all this for himself, in his visit to Georgetown, the capital of British Guiana. The colonial medical officers were eager for a progam, and it was decided that a start would be made in the Peter's Hall District, a few miles from Georgetown and on the bank of the Demerara River.

It was agreed that the Sanitary Commission's program would be modified in one important way. Instead of dispensary demonstrations, an intensive effort would be made, as on Knotts Island, North Carolina, to find and treat every case of hookworm infection in the selected area. Returning to Washington, where Dr. John A. Ferrell had been holding the fort as assistant director, Rose chose a Rockefeller Sanitary Commission field director from Mississippi, Dr. Hector H. Howard, to be director for the West Indies, at $2,000 a year plus allowances. Associates remembered Howard for three things: He was a fundamentalist in religion, always carried a Bible, and swore a lot. Strong in his opinions, Howard made redemption from hookworms seem close at hand. It might also be added that he possessed two primary attributes of a good public health field man—he liked details and he never seemed to tire.

Howard landed in Georgetown on March 9, 1914, and the operating program of the new International Health Commission dated from that moment. He quickly found that, compared to British Guiana, fighting hookworm in Mississippi had been simple. In the first place, the climate in the American South was on the side of eradication; during the chill winter weather the hookworm eggs in the soil rarely could hatch and larvae could not become active; in any event, most people wore shoes in the winter. Thus, there was a natural break of several months each year in the cycle of reinfection.

British Guiana, with its long summer and winter rainy seasons and continuous heat and barefooted inhabitants, provided an uninterrupted opportunity for reinfection. Here Howard now faced a population of East Indians, Portuguese, Chinese, and Negroes. The East Indians, the main carriers of infection, were not tolerant of discipline once they had served out their labor contracts; the Portuguese were highly susceptible to severe infection but indifferent to help; the Chinese were disinclined to take medicine unless in acute pain; the Negroes were least responsive of all because of ignorance and illiteracy.

But Howard translated his health stories, language by language, into allegorical tales of demons that turned into worms, taking full advantage of the general conviction in the West Indies that the woods and air were full of evil spirits, all eager for victims.

The plan of operation called for two separate undertakings. The staff of the International Health Commission would find, and treat until it cured, all infected persons in the area. A government staff would undertake a latrine program aimed at stopping soil pollution and preventing reinfection.

The required I.H.D. staff included the field director, a clerk, three microscopists, six to eight nurses, and three office employees—fourteen to sixteen in all. This team was entirely geared, in its educational as well as technological work, to a treatment objective.

The first step in this intensive treatment program called for a complete census of persons living in the treatment area. "This in itself is a considerable undertaking," Howard conceded. The native villages were crowded, some inhabitants had a tendency to move, and others had no permanent home. To keep track of residents, census takers found it convenient to write a number on each house with a heavy red crayon and then enter it in their census book. The final objective of Howard's team was to write the word "cured" after the name of every person listed at every house. This required at least two and sometimes three or more purges with thymol and Epsom salts a week apart, also a considerable undertaking.

Howard, with the vigorous cooperation of the British medical officer in the Peter's Hall District, Dr. J. E. A. Ferguson, was so successful in the first four months (March through June) and told such a glowing story on a return trip to the United States that Rose adopted the intensive method for the continuing program in the United States. It became the pattern for scores of overseas campaigns to come.

Howard extended his intensive program from British Guiana to Dutch Guiana, Trinidad, Antigua, Grenada, St. Lucia, and St. Vincent during the next three years. The experience was so similar throughout these seven colonies with a total population of 167,000 that it can be quickly summarized. Ninety-nine percent of the population was examined and 59 percent was found to be infected. Seventy-five percent of the infected was cured, 8 percent left the area, and 17 percent remained in the area uncured.

The Commission's Publication No. 1, *The Eradication of Ankylostomiasis in British Guiana*, in which Howard reported his 1914 experience, became so much in demand with extension of the program to other countries, that a first edition cannot be found today.

Dr. Howard said knowledge of hookworm disease and its transmission was so complete that "it has been an easy task to elaborate a perfect theory for the prevention of the disease." If persons who had the disease could be found and cured and soil pollution prevented, "then, theoretically, complete eradication is an accomplished fact." He acknowledged that what seemed simple on paper was not so in fact.

There were many obstacles, but these all boiled down to one: lack of cooperation by people with hookworm. The hookworm program remained the most pressing business of the Foundation for the next ten years. During the peak years, the annual reports of the I. H. D. carried a composite cumulative table of all persons examined and treated for hookworm infection through the world from 1910 on. As an indication of subsiding interest, this table was published for the last time in 1925, although expenditures for hookworm control remained substantial and did not tail off until 1930.

In sixteen years, more than 5 million persons were microscopically examined for hookworm in forty different states and countries. More than 3 million were found to be infected, or about 60 percent. Some 2.7 million persons received two or more treatments.

Inasmuch as these programs were simply variations of the common theme, their interest derives not so much from the conquest of disease—although many were cured—as from the personalities of the doctors and their adventures in answering, each in his own way, the often-repeated question of one I. H. D. doctor: "Why do we do it?"

7

What Vermifuge Do You Use?

The hookworm doctors, as one of them remarked, had to have the hearts of lions to inflict such punishment as vermifuges and purges on a population, no matter what the benefit. In their office on lower Broadway, however, Rose and his staff might have found a more suitable analogy in the stock market. From one field report and one year to the next, their fortunes as investors in the well-being of mankind rose and fell. If the men in the field had to be lion-hearted, these entrepreneurs of good health had to have nerves as strong and tuneful as piano wire.

As time went on, field men longed for a better hookworm treatment. Until 1917, patients were treated exclusively with thymol. From 1917 to 1922, there was a great swing to oil of chenopodium. From 1922 until 1929, carbon tetrachloride was the rule. After that, the modern treatment of choice, tetrachlorethylene, achieved general acceptance and since then has withstood all competition, although experimentation with other drugs has continued, in hope for something still better. When physicians swing from one drug to another in the treatment of a common disease, it can only mean doctor-patient dissatisfaction with what is available.

The ideal vermifuge should remove nearly all worms in most cases in one dose. It should not only be safe in carefully selected cases and in the correct dosage, but well-nigh foolproof in any case and any amount. It should be wholly predictable, meaning that it has to be purified and standardized. It must be made at a reasonable cost. It should not be unpleasant to take and should produce no uncomfortable aftereffects. All this is asking a lot in a drug that, first off, must be toxic enough to kill a living organism—the worm.

Stiles had said that a human being wrecked by the "laziness bug" could be restored to health for fifty cents' worth of thymol and Epsom salts. However, the great drawback to thymol was that it often took not one but two or three and sometimes five or ten treatments to achieve a cure. This, with a purge before and after each time, left the patient weak and unwilling to come back for more. Resistance to treatment certainly was not lessened when the drug caused nausea, a burning sensation in the stomach, or a headache.

It sometimes happened, though rarely, that a person died through a sensitivity to the drug or some dietary indiscretion, such as drinking alcohol or eating fatty foods instead of fasting before treatment. Alcohol and fat acted as solvents of the drug and are themselves rapidly absorbed into the blood stream. This was the purpose of the post-treatment purge, to rid the intestinal tract of the drug before the body could absorb it.

When the first news of oil of chenopodium got around, the Board's field directors were ready for a change. Dr. Wilhelm A. Schüffner (1867-1949), a German, had begun using this vermifuge in Sumatra, in the Dutch East Indies, as early as 1900, and by 1913 was able to report on the treatment of 100,000 cases. Results appeared so successful that the I.H.D. asked Schüffner for instructions on the use of chenopodium and these were circulated to field directors.

Chenopodium is a weed, a mealy herb, variously known as Jerusalem oak, goosefoot, wormseed, or lamb's-quarters. The value of its oily, odorous seed in killing various intestinal worms was a matter of folklore before science took chenopodium over. It had the advantage of being highly effective against roundworms, often found as intestinal neighbors of hookworms.

Tests indicated that oil of chenopodium in the maximum safe dose was slightly more powerful than thymol as well as being cheaper and easier to administer and less unpleasant to take. While the oil had an offensive taste and odor, these drawbacks could be concealed by swigging the drug in molasses, honey, or strong coffee mixed with brown sugar.

As experience accumulated, the results were variable and reports in sharp conflict. Some doctors pronounced this drug "96 percent effective in one dose"; others mentioned "alarming symptoms, and sometimes death." The symptoms seemed to be about the same as for thymol, and were blamed in part upon variations in the purity and potency of the drug used. Deaths were mainly due to "overdoses." In addition, it was found that chenopodium did not expel all the worms, but caused some female worms to stop laying eggs for a few days, thus producing a false appearance of cure when the patient's feces was examined again. Some doctors overcame the deficiencies of thymol and chenopodium by a shotgun approach; they gave both at once. This combined not only the advantages but the disadvantages.

Obviously, the ideal treatment had not yet been discovered. On this point, Dr. Sylvester M. Lambert, (1882-1947) was eloquent. He was a square-jawed, near-sighted, rough-and-ready, colorful American doctor of tropical medicine, a former physician for the United Fruit Company in Costa Rica. In 1920, the I.H.D. hired Lambert and sent him to New Guinea and later to the Fiji Islands.

After four years of fighting hookworms with oil of chenopodium in Queensland, New Guinea, the Fiji Islands, Tonga, the Gilbert Islands, and even more remote islands such as Rotumah, Pitcairn, and Christmas, Lambert was frankly depressed, as he recounted, in *Yankee Doctor in Paradise* (1941). It was not that he had to work with woolly-haired blacks whose fathers were cannibals and themselves were sometimes suspected of eating the "long pig," but because "I was like a fireman with a leaky hose, trying to stop a blaze at one end of a building while an incendiary poured gasoline on the other. The government health authorities had a right to mourn over the Foundation's recent attempts to kill the all-pervading parasite. Everywhere I went I saw how little the good work had accomplished." The grinding disappointments of examination, treatment, re-examination, and retreatment, he said, drove many good men out of public health work.

In Suva, the Fiji capital, one late afternoon in February 1922, Lambert picked up the *Journal* of the American Medical Association for November 19, 1921, on his desk. By chance, he opened the *Journal* and saw an article entitled, "The use of Carbon Tetrachloride for the Removal of Hookworms," by Maurice C. Hall,

Ph.D., D.V.M., Senior Zoologist, United States Bureau of Animal Industry.

What Stiles, also a Bureau of Animal Industry zoologist, had been to hookworm sanitation, Hall was to hookworm therapeutics—a true prophet. This was his first revelation. Hall had noticed that animals anesthetized with chloroform ($CHCl_3$) frequently expelled intestinal parasites afterward, indicating that the chloroform had vermifuge action even when inhaled. The anesthetic itself would have been just the thing for worming dogs and cats, if it were not so unpredictably lethal. He set about testing other hydrocarbons, hitting finally upon a relative of chloroform, carbon tetrachloride (CCl_4), until then distinguished only as a cheap dry-cleaning fluid and fire extinguisher. Trying it in dogs, he found this tetrachloride just about 100 percent effective in getting rid of hookworms in one dose of 3cc for a twenty-two pound dog. Although he suspected there might be liver damage, as sometimes happened with chloroform, he could see none in his experimental animals.

Knowing that public health doctors were dissatisfied with thymol and chenopodium, Hall decided to try carbon tetrachloride himself. Three hours after a light breakfast and a cigar, he downed about three teaspoonfuls and went about his work, smoking more cigars and eating at the usual times. Except for belching a little carbon tetrachloride and a mild warmth in his abdomen, he noticed nothing. Eventually, he experienced a laxative effect. Borrowing a few monkeys from the Hygienic Laboratory of the Public Health Service, he gave them much larger doses of the drug. They lost interest in food for a day or two but that was all. Hall suggested that hookworm doctors might wish to test his impression that carbon tetrachloride was more effective and safer than the drugs they were using. One advantage might be that they could eliminate the purgative, and certainly CCl_4 was far cheaper than thymol or oil of chenopodium.

This was all the encouragement Lambert needed. He scrounged around in the laboratory and found a big brown bottle of carbon tetrachloride. He then went to Dr. Aubrey Montague, the British chief medical officer in Suva, and showed him the article and the bottle. Montague read the article and looked at the bottle. "Lambert, try anything," he sighed. Lambert went to the native hospital and selected four East Indians with hookworm disease. He gave them a dose of salts and returned early the next morning and gave them a three-teaspoon dose each from the big brown bottle. As soon as they had swallowed it, he began to worry, he said. "Doctors have to become hardened to death," he commented, "otherwise they couldn't remain in practice. But experimental killing is a different thing. If any of these Hindus died I'd have the weight on my soul. Not only that, I'd lose my job . . ."

Lambert had no appetite for breakfast. Why hadn't he taken the drug himself, before trying it on others, as Hall had done? *But Hall had taken it.* Still, Hall was a healthy man and these poor fellows were frail and sickly. Lambert was sitting in his office later in the day, feeling wretched, when his medical technician came in.

"That tetrachloride—"

"Are they dead?" asked Lambert stiffly.

"Dead?" The technician waved his hands. "They're all jumping out of bed and simply spouting hookworms!"

The patients continued to do this for three days and,

as Lambert said, "Doctors gathered around our hook-worm count like baseball fans around the box score."

Lambert continued his experiments and grew more and more excited about the possibilities of CCl_4. He wrote a careful letter about it to the Rockefeller Foundation in New York. Back came a cablegram from "Rockfound." It said: "Forbid use. We do not experiment with human life." Lambert showed the message to Montague, observing, "I'm forbidden to play with fire extinguishers." The British doctor pondered the situation and at last said he did not intend to give up tetrachloride. He was going to authorize it for use in all institutions under the authority of the government of Fiji. Inasmuch as Lambert was assigned to him, Montague authorized Lambert as his subordinate to continue using the drug. Whatever happened was now on British heads. The Foundation entered no further objection, and Lambert thereupon began a mass-treatment program.

Carbon tetrachloride sometimes produced a mild excitation, some dizziness, and drowsiness. These qualities made it attractive to the Fiji Islanders, who used it as an excuse for beating drums, dancing, and running in the streets.

It seems to be a precept of clinical medicine that pride in a new treatment precedes a fall, it happens so often. Lambert had his fall after the successful treatment of 42,000 persons without mishap during 1922. Then, receiving a new supply of the drug, he treated 8,000 more. Three died—two East Indian boys, five and seven years old, and an East Indian woman. The first boy, it turned out, had taken oil of chenopodium and not tetrachloride and had no purge; the second had a congenital malformation of the intestine. The woman was an alcoholic. He had four more treatment deaths in

1923, all children heavily infested with roundworms as well as hookworms.

It was now apparent that Hall and Lambert had overlooked something. The "Yankee doctor in Paradise" was not, of course, the only field man trying carbon tetrachloride. Dr. Wilson G. Smillie experimented with it in Brazil and soon noticed that it made alcoholics deathly sick, even though it did not necessarily kill them. He suspected that their livers were already in bad shape and suggested that the drug was causing fatty degeneration of the liver. It was therefore necessary to follow the same precautions with the new as the old vermifuges, including the use of the post-treatment purge to guard against absorption of the drug into the blood stream. Another fact eventually observed was that patients were much more susceptible to "carbon tet" poisoning when their blood calcium was low, a phenomenon frequently present when there was a heavy infestation of roundworms as well as hookworms. An additional hazard was that roundworms occasionally would form a ball and cause an intestinal obstruction.

Lambert had no further trouble, and in 1933 was able to report the treatment in the South Pacific islands of 240,000 persons with carbon tetrachloride. His total treatment deaths remained at seven, one in 34,000 overall; after 1923 he had 150,000 consecutive tetrachloride treatments without a death.

There was no question either that carbon tetrachloride was more efficient than its predecessors or that it could be potential dynamite in careless hands. Dissatisfied, Maurice Hall went back to the laboratory and, in his second and greater discovery in 1925, emerged with tetrachloroethylene (C_2Cl_4). Hall reported that tetrachloroethylene without benefit of purge removed all hookworms in 89 percent of his dogs and 99.5 percent of the hookworms in all dogs. As usual, Hall took a dose of the drug himself and noticed nothing untoward except, when he went to bed that night, he had a dream involving a floating sensation. The investigators said the drug was equal to or possibly a little better than carbon tetrachloride in efficiency and safety, and had a pleasanter taste and odor. It deserved "cautious test in human medicine under hospital conditions."

Cautious testing was exactly what it got. The I.H.D. men were just straightening out the details of safe carbon tetrachloride treatment and not eager to take on anything else like it. Hall wrote Lambert in May 1925 to try tetrachloroethylene. Lambert did so, on thirteen patients in New Hebrides, and could not see that it offered any advantage, as he reported in December.

Meanwhile the I.H.D. began making grants to Dr. Paul D. Lamson (1884-1962), first at Johns Hopkins and then at Vanderbilt University, to investigate the pharmacology and toxicology of hookworm drugs. In 1929, the Lamson group in the Vanderbilt Department of Pharmacology put tetrachloroethylene back in the hookworm news by showing that in animals it could be used with far greater safety than either oil of chenopodium or carbon tetrachloride for the reason that, quite unlike the others, it was insoluble in the intestinal tract. From that time on the superior merits of tetrachloroethylene were gradually proved, although it was many years before doctors were convinced that they should give up the debilitating cathartic, always used as a hedge against liver damage.

Ironically, Hall's first discovery, carbon tetrachloride, made an immediate splash and then ran into trouble, whereas his second and lasting contribution was eyed skeptically and required five years before it caught on. In the last thirty years tetrachloroethylene has been used in millions of patients, many of them sick and dragging, but only one death has been reported, that of an emaciated beggar in India. Occasionally, the drug causes giddiness, inebriation, and sleepiness, but its undesirable effects are minor. The noon-to-noon or sundown-to-noon periods of fasting and purging with previous drugs are no longer necessary, and the patient can usually go about his business with but little inconvenience. In modern times, it has been recognized that drastic purging is itself a menace to health; it can make a sick person sicker, or even kill him without being blamed. Given in gelatin capsules, tetrachloroethylene can be counted on to knock out 90 percent of a patient's hookworms in one dose (yet it is not ideal—10 percent remain to breed anew).

Tetrachloroethylene came into its ascendancy as the I.H.D. hookworm-control sun was setting. With this new weapon, the national, state, and local health services that the I.H.D. helped develop carried on the good work. The numbers treated annually presently exceeded the entire Rockefeller effort.

8

Human Nature

Wickliffe Rose and his hookworm doctors could, if they wished, literally see the blood of their treated patients grow redder and richer. In anemic persons, the hemoglobin index definitely rose following treatment. Yet such good results alone could not conquer hookworm; as long as there were some uncured persons and soil pollution, reinfections occurred and good results were completely undone. Only changes in toilet habits could eradicate the parasite in the human intestine. It is incredible how much ignorance, superstition, and prejudice surrounds the function of elimination. Some of the most colorful documentation on this score came from Dr. Wilson G. Smillie, with the I.H.D. for twelve years—1916 to 1928—before going on to Harvard and later Cornell as a professor of public health administration and chairman of his department.

In Brazil, "Jack" Smillie, then in his early thirties, presented an imposing sight on the hookworm trail, riding into an Indian village on horseback, with his high hat, beard, horn-rimmed glasses, and pointed leather boots, followed by Solomao, his Indian bodyguard and technician, equipped with a field kit, pistol, rifle, and machete. Solomao had been an attendant in a reform school, and had the distinction of having been a bandit and having killed a man. But he was a good lab technician.

The Indians commonly mistook the white doctor as a messenger either of God or of the Devil, and treated him accordingly. It was Smillie's custom to present himself to the leading citizen of the village, the chief or possibly the storekeeper, and explain his mission—to find the hookworm and cure those who gave it shelter. When the Indians were persuaded and had gathered, the doctor palpated their spleens and Solomao drew a sample of blood from ear or finger. The test for hemoglobin was then made in the nearest dark room, by holding the blood specimen before a candle and estimating red cells from the degree of translucence. The procedure provided a fair index to the presence of anemia. If the test was positive, a fecal examination would then be done.

In one village, Smillie and Solomao had tied their horses before the store in a one-street village and assembled a group of Indians in the back room of the shop for testing. Suddenly the room emptied, Smillie related, and nobody could be called back. The storekeeper explained that the *curandeiro*—the local quack doctor—was on his way over, having told the people that a representative of the Devil was examining their blood in order that he might be able to sell their souls to the ruler of Hell.

Soon a crowd came back up the street, carrying machetes, pitchforks, and scythes, the *curandeiro* in the lead and urging them to rout the Devil's agent. Smillie and Solomao mounted their horses and rode out of town.

They made a house-to-house survey in another village, but the doors of the mud-covered, palm-thatched huts were slammed in their faces. They were going back to their roominghouse when a wild, ragged-looking man with the broad bare feet of the Indian peasant broke out of the woods and brandished a gun and knife at them. "If you come back to my house, I'll kill you!" he shouted. "Then we won't come back," Smillie advised him. "But what's the trouble?" The Indian looked at the doctor's pointed boots: "Just you dare take off those boots and show me your feet." Smillie pulled off one boot and sock. The Indian seemed dumfounded to see a pale, soft-looking foot so unlike his own. He then said he did not think anyone could wear a pointed boot unless it concealed a cloven hoof! "We became friends," said Smillie. "He felt sorry for me with feet like that."

Smillie and Solomao made an expedition into the Matto Grosso, to an Indian reservation at Bananal. They were told the Indians would have nothing to do with them; this was the home grounds of the bandits of three nations and strangers were unwelcome. As they neared the village a boy came galloping toward them, shouting that an Indian had been bitten by a snake. Only the month before, it seemed, a man there had died of snake-bite.

They spurred on and met a Scottish missionary who lived near the village with his wife and two children. He said it was true, and the doctor had arrived at the right time. He led Smillie to the patient, who was lying in his skin bed, pale with pain and fear. He had killed the snake and it lay nearby. While the villagers gathered around, Smillie found the double-puncture wound of the snake's fangs in the man's arm. Fearing that he might have arrived too late, he applied a tourniquet and with his knife made an incision through the wound, a deep cut in the form of a cross; the blood flowed.

He noticed an awed stirring among the Indians, and the missionary explained: "You have just made the sign of the cross. If this man gets better, it will be a great help to me." There was nothing left to do. Smillie remembered an old folk remedy in Colorado, where he was born. He called for a chicken, quickly wrung its neck, bled it, and split it open. He applied it as a poultice to the wound, the dubious theory being that it helped draw the poison. The Indians were again impressed; as the missionary interpreted it to Smillie, they thought the soul of the chicken was being sent to heaven in place of the man's. When the man appeared to be getting better, Smillie ordered the family to bury the snake and chicken together. The victim recovered, to the relief of the missionary, of Smillie, and of course Solomao, who had argued against the visit.

The village was now at the doctor's disposal. They found a great deal of hookworm infection and treated it. They had the cooperation of everybody except the chief's small son. He hid in the woods, unconvinced that the white man was not the Devil. The father, after undergoing diagnosis and treatment himself, talked to the boy, who agreed to send the doctor a fecal specimen but insisted on remaining in the woods. In due course, he was pronounced infected and Smillie treated him by remote control, sending out the vermifuge capsules and then a dose of Epsom salts.

Unfortunately, on rare occasions a patient thus treated may suffer a temporary bowel paralysis, due to a nervous spasm. This constitutes a medical emergency until the bowels move. This happened in the case of the fearful boy, and now Smillie and Solomao saw they were in danger. The boy was limp in his father's arms, with eyes closed, when the chief brought him out of the woods and stood before the doctor. Smillie first tried hot coffee. When this did not work, he prepared an enema. As he took the boy from the father, the lad's eyes opened, he found himself in the arms of the Devil, and the purge suddenly worked. "It was the only time I ever scared anybody back to life," commented Smillie.

In some places, the sanitary doctors and engineers were able to get people pretty well stirred up about sanitary privies and worked remarkable transformations. For example, the Hattiesburg (Mississippi) *Tribune* cooperated in the soil sanitation launched in the South in 1916 by listing each week the names of families that had brought their latrines up to State Board of Health standards, the list being headed: "Forrest County Leads the State in Rural Sanitation." Another stimulating device, employed in the communities of Pearl River County, Mississippi, was the public posting of a large map showing the location of every house in town. As each householder met minimum sanitary standards his particular dot was ringed. The map became an increasing source of embarrassment to the unringed as the program progressed, and, of course, a great local conversation piece.

Dr. Milford E. Barnes, in Siam, encountered a Buddhist priest who, forbidden by his religion to take life, had refused to treat his malaria with quinine after being told it would "kill the germs." Barnes avoided this mistake and persuaded the priest to take the hookworm medicine by demonstrating in the washings from his stool that the worms were still alive when expelled.

Some Siamese were unhappy with oil of chenopodium because its strong and pungent odor suggested evil spirits, and also because the drug sometimes gave them sensations of dizziness and tingling. They attributed these to "wind," a serious affliction. One woman who felt "wind" escaping from her heel tied a black thread around the calf of her leg to trap it and then took a large knife and laid open the flesh to "let the wind out."

In Ceylon, a British colony, resistance to examination and treatment took various forms, political as well as religious. Singhalese medicine men said that purgatives must not be taken when it was raining, an idea that was readily accepted because few latrines offered protection against the downpour and leeches were more active when the leaves and ground were wet. Because it rained so often, this attitude handicapped the hookworm program.

During World War I, field directors all the way from the West to the East Indies encountered resistance when they attempted to take a census of a village. A flood of derogatory rumors seemed to precede them wherever they went in Ceylon. One was to the effect that Germany would win the war in six months. The vermifuge capsules were really small bombs which would remain in the body until the Germans took possession of the island. Then the bombs would burst inside and kill the coolies so no one would be left to work the plantations—a variation of the "scorched earth" idea.

Dr. Lambert, though in some despair of controlling hookworm, struck a rich vein of anthropological lore in his nearly twenty years as a roving public health officer among the hundreds of islands scattered across six million square miles of the South Pacific. He found that even Fijians who had accepted Christianity from the missionaries regarded magic as their true religion, though loath to admit the fact to white men.

Jinxes up to and including voodoo deaths from fright could be imposed merely by hiring a witch doctor to "point a bone." It was lethal from any distance as long as you knew it was pointing your way. Melanesians, Polynesians, Micronesians all felt the same way about these matters. *Ndrau-ni-kau,* meaning "magic of leaves," was the highest in a hierarchy of curses. The witch doctor obtained a bit of clothing or hair or feces from his victim. These things, mixed with leaves, were shut up in a bamboo joint or a bottle. The ritual involved taking a *ndrau-ni-kau* to the graveyard and invoking a *tevoro,* or evil spirit. Once the curse was on, the victim was to die in four days, unless he could get a rival sorcerer to pray off the curse and, best of all, turn it back on the enemy.

The unspoiled, friendly Polynesians of Sikiana took Lambert's hookworm lecture, in pidgin English, as a great joke, yet were too kind to refuse his request for specimens. Likewise, among Papuans, he had no trouble getting specimens although he ran into a strange native reticence to giving one's name to be written on the label. The individual would stand mute or, at best, whisper his name to a bystander who would pass it on, also in a whisper. To speak a name out loud would be to invite the spirit of a dead relative to come to roost on the owner, so to speak.

Cannibalism still persisted among some of the tribes during the 1920's, but was carried on in the utmost secrecy out of fear of punishment from the white man's policemen and soldiers. Lambert was warned against going to Malekula, in the New Hebrides, where the French had added guns, liquor, and opium to a native cannibalism more recently sublimated in ritualistic sacrifices of pigs in barbecues. The doctor went anyway.

"I was told," he said, "that if I asked for specimens on Malekula the Big Nambas would either take a pot shot at me or run howling into the jungle. Even the missionized ones feared that I was collecting fragments of excreta for purposes of witch-doctoring." Even so, Lambert managed to make enough worm counts following purges to estimate that the New Hebrides hookworm infection rate was more than 94 percent.

Lambert could not resist trying his luck and risking his life on Rennell, in the Solomon Islands. Rennell is a coral island, a jungle on top of sheer cliffs dropping into the sea. Its estimated 1,500 inhabitants in 1930 were just moving from the Shell Age into the Iron Age, having skipped the Stone Age. They would trade their women for anything of iron or steel, having nothing else that appealed to the crews of trading ships. They had killed some missionaries who came a few years before; this they admitted, but they denied eating them. It was not their fashion, they said.

The Rennellese were unarmed and friendly enough; they came out to the ship and climbed all over it, looked into everything, and would not leave. Lambert and his assistants eased into the situation and talked about the "senake in bel," or snake in the belly, as the hookworm was described in pidgin. But the health men could not get the idea across, as they had with Fijians and others. These tall, well-muscled men with dark olive skins, long black hair tied in a bun at the back, pierced noses, tattooed bodies, and tapa loincloths had no conception of disease except as a punishment from their God Who Walked along the Sky and dwelt in the head of Big Master, their chief. Lambert set up a tent and microscope on the beach and offered the people tin containers. He was unable to make them understand what was wanted until one of the ship's crew demonstrated.

Then there was, as Lambert related, a bedlam of frightened yells and small boys came scampering out, hands in air, mouths open, screaming. The sailor explained, "When I put the specimen in and closed the lid, they stared as if they were accusing me of an atrocious crime." Lambert's Rennellese interpreter presently came back, followed by natives now carrying spears and clubs for the first time. The interpreter said, "Master, dis fellow he something altogether tabu. Him he tabu too much," meaning "very much." He suggested that if they went on looking for hookworm eggs, the Big Master would kill them and him, too.

However, the Big Master had invited Lambert and his group to a festival at a lake, eight miles inland. Lambert thought he might try to change the Big Master's mind, being aware, as all white men were not, that the Polynesian word *tabu* had flexibility—what was tabu at the moment was not necessarily verboten at another time.

Lambert presented the Big Master with an ax but did not dare mention hookworms. However, his go-between did, and after a parley, told the doctor that, if he would give him the tins, it might be all right to get a few specimens. Lambert offered two fishhooks per specimen, and in this way managed to collect sixteen specimens in a population of 1,500. More than half were infected. Each donor suspiciously watched Lambert in the entire examination of the specimens, which he did crudely and hurriedly under the circumstances. He did not use the microscope. His patrons were not satisfied they were free of black magic until the specimens were thrown into a hole in the sand. An exacting worm count, following treatment and involving much washing and screening of the specimen, would have been a capital offense, he figured.

There was nothing like a latrine on Rennell Island.

The natives dug a hole in the sand and carefully covered their deposits—to keep it out of some witch's sight.

Throughout the South Seas, Lambert found the hookworm rate as variable (from a little or none to 90 or 100 percent) as the reception he received. Toilet habits were equally variable, generally consisting of going behind the nearest bush. In the high mountains of New Britain, however, he was in for a surprise. Among a fierce, savage, cannibalistic tribe, he found but few parasites and "latrines as scientifically constructed as if endorsed by the International Health Board." These were pits twenty-five to thirty feet deep, covered with a platform of timbers. Hookworm larvae could not get out and flies would not enter the dark depths. Lambert learned that these cess pits were there *before* the first white expedition into those parts, a punitive campaign intended to put a stop to man-eating. The only explanation that Lambert could elicit of why they used this kind of latrine was: "It is the fashion."

In even the briefest pursuit of the Rockefeller Foundation along the privy path, the bored-hole latrine stands out as a milestone. It was "the Foundation's enthusiasm" at the time that Victor Heiser visited Lambert in Fiji in 1928. The bored-hole latrine (B.H.L.) was introduced by the Dutch in Java and had an arresting simplicity about it, as an engineering idea. It was a hole, from ten to twenty-five inches in diameter, bored into the ground with a hand auger to a depth of fifteen to twenty-five feet. The East Indian squatted on a concrete slab capping the hole and when it was filled presumably dug another.

Lambert preferred the large, deep pit covered with a polished concrete slab. The problem in many parts of the tropics is about the same today as where the I.H.D. left it. The pit privy, B.H.L., aqua privy, bucket or box-

and-can privy, trench latrine, overhung privy (over ocean or river), and chemical toilet all have practical disadvantages. The septic tank is most useful and satisfactory, but costly.

In China, it is worth noting, the hookworm doctors were up against not promiscuous, behind-the-bush defecation but an ancient, organized system of soil pollution wherever there was farming. The hookworm-control problem was so formidable, in fact, that, as in India, the I.H.D. was inclined to look and experiment but not leap into an intensive treatment and sanitation program.

The idea that bodily wastes are worthless is deeply imbedded in the Western thought, as one can recognize by reflection on various Anglo-Saxon expressions regarding the subject. In Chinese culture quite the opposite has been true. Indeed, the city people traditionally hoard their "night soil" and sell it to the farmers as fertilizer. This custom was blamed by various medical authorities as the source of widespread hookworm infection in China.

In 1923 and 1924, the Foundation sent the China Hookworm Commission, under Dr. William W. Cort of Johns Hopkins, to investigate the question. The Chinese procedure was to compost human feces with straw and clay, as a dry manure, or store it wet in jars (*kongs*) and then, as needed, haul this night soil off to the fields by wheelbarrow or carrying pole. Certain men made a living doing this.

In an exhaustive report, published in 1926, Cort included some surprising observations. Hookworm infection was a great problem among men, women, and children who cultivated mulberry trees (to feed silkworms). They used night soil around the base of the trees and during the wet days, in the second picking of the leaves, frequently developed ground itch and anemia. In short, what the silkworm did for the farmer the hookworm undid in ill health. Night soil was also used in rice cultivation, but contrary to what had been previously believed, there was little or no hookworm infection associated with the rice fields. The reason was that after fertilization the fields were kept constantly under water during the growing period. In this much water, the hookworm eggs did not develop. Whereas a little moisture on warm ground aids and abets the hookworm larvae, too much water drowns them.

Since the use of night soil, running to an estimated 24 million tons a year at that time, was an economic necessity and also part of thrifty Chinese agricultural rites formulated a thousand years before the Christian era, Cort was inclined to agree that human manure was a basis of Chinese civilization and not something that could be flushed down the drain. He could think of little to recommend except that night soil be used in rice but not in mulberry cultivation.

9

Getting off the Hookworm Hook

Wickliffe Rose put nothing in the record specifying when he gave up his hope of eradicating hookworm *somewhere*. As rational and perceptive as he was, he did come to recognize that nature—*human* nature—had him licked. Raymond B. Fosdick, who became the personal legal counsel of John D. Rockefeller, Jr., in 1912 and was a close observer of the Rockefeller philanthropic family from that time on, recalls that about 1920 Rose confided to him, "We made a great mistake when we used the word *eradication*. That was our dream, but it just couldn't be done." Yet Rose's ego investment apparently was not such, nor were his interests so narrow, that he could imagine himself as the tragic figure in Poe's morbid poem about the conquering worm.

He now felt a démarche was in order. Writing his 1919 annual report, he noted that hookworm relief measures had been in progress in Puerto Rico since Ashford began them in 1904, yet a recent survey had disclosed an 80 percent rural infection rate and three-quarters of rural homes without latrines. Puerto Rico, he said, offered "a striking example of the hopelessness of treatment cam-

paigns unless they are accompanied by good sanitation."
This was the first time this determined optimist had admitted any note of hopelessness into his reports, although the feeling was by this time fairly general among
his men in the field. It went without saying, good sanitation was the stumbling block.

The situation, Rose wrote, "suggests that perhaps
the work is being carried out with a lack of scientific information on certain points concerning which definitive
knowledge is indispensable if complete control is to be
achieved."

This statement constituted not only a pleasing touch
of candor but a startling turn-about in viewpoint. The
International Health Commission's primary excuse for
being, as that of the Rockefeller Sanitary Commission
before it, held that the knowledge necessary to eradicate
hookworm disease was available but was not being applied—that there was a gap between scientific discovery
and the application of findings.

Events now pulled Rose, most uncomfortably, in
two directions. One was to maintain his original stance
as head of a social action agency carrying out measures
that would make people healthier. The other was to
accept the need for research and shift the emphasis to a
search for new scientific knowledge that would overcome the failures rising out of experience.

Hookworm control now bristled with question
marks. We already have explored the protracted problem in therapeutics, which did not show great promise
until laboratory scientists came to the rescue of the public health doctors in the field. There were other questions:

Where was the worm most vulnerable? Was there
any way of attacking eggs or larvae in the polluted soil?

In fact, what was really known about the parasite when it was at the mercy of all outdoors? Arthur Looss hadn't done much with this part of its life cycle. How long could eggs and larvae survive in the soil? How far could the larva migrate? One man figured it at forty yards in any direction. But here was the Dutch observer, August Baermann, with a new apparatus for detecting the larvae in soil samples, and evidence that extensive migration was the bunk.

What about the host? Many people carried worms with no apparent ill effects. Why? Was it simply a matter of a good diet, adequate in proteins and iron? Was there an immunity that could be induced and measured in antibodies? Or was it all a matter of how many worms a man had in his small intestine?

Until 1920, the only real laboratory scientist on the I.H.D. staff was Dr. Samuel T. Darling (1872-1925), who had been chief of laboratories for the Isthmian Canal Commission in the Panama Canal Zone from 1906 to 1915. Darling, medical descendant of a long line of clergymen, had been one of General William C. Gorgas's right-hand men during the construction of the Canal and had taken part in the yellow-fever and malaria control programs there. A handsome, brilliant, temperamental man, optimistic but critical, with a shock of dark hair, piercing eyes, a large mustache and a small goatee, Darling from 1915 to 1918 disentangled hookworm disease from malaria as causes of anemia in Malaya, Java, and Fiji. In 1918, he became professor of hygiene and director of laboratories in the Medical School of São Paulo, Brazil, with young Dr. Smillie as his assistant, collaborator, and successor. Darling's career ended tragically. Recovered from an operation for a brain tumor at Johns

Hopkins in 1921, he was killed in an automobile accident in 1925, in Syria, at the age of fifty-three.

Darling became a specialist in field research, which for him meant taking the laboratory and its methods to the scene of infection. He was the first man to reduce hookworm scatology to a mathematical basis. While still in the Orient, he began counting the worms a treated patient expelled to measure the severity of infection and the results of treatment. His methods were crude and required refinement, but he managed to dispose of the all-or-none way of defining hookworm disease. Continuing his research in Brazil, Darling, with Smillie, showed there was a lot of difference between hookworm *infection* and hookworm *disease*. The difference lay in the *worm burden*, meaning the number of worms hooked into an individual's jejunum. The presence or absence of anemia—in fact the degree of anemia—depended to a large extent on the number of worms that had tapped the blood stream.

As one example of where this amplification of knowledge led, Darling and Smillie found that the significant effect of wearing or not wearing shoes was not so much in the incidence but the intensity of infection. Brazilian plantation workers who wore shoes averaged twenty-seven worms per infection as compared to 255 in infected workers who went barefoot. These researchers also showed that persons between fifteen and thirty-nine years old have a strong resistance to hookworm disease in comparison with children and older persons.

Darling and Smillie further emphasized that what made the difference between light and heavy infestation was opportunity for repeated reinfection, inasmuch as hookworms cannot multiply within the body but must pursue their bizarre in-and-out cycle to reproduce. The severity of infection was found to be proportional to the length of time of exposure (working in the fields). It took both children and newly arrived workers from four to eight years to acquire a heavy infestation, their worm burden being eight times heavier than those who had worked in the fields two years or less.

The fact that women had less intense infections than men also added up. Girls hoed in the field until they were eighteen or nineteen and then they usually married and assumed household duties that reduced their chances of further infection.

Such distinctions were useful. They suggested, as Darling was the first to advocate, that in a hookworm-saturated population it was a waste of time to collect specimens and make microscopic diagnoses before treatment. It was more economical to treat everybody except, of course, persons too weak or sick to withstand the ordeal of treatment. By the same token, the differentiation between infection and disease eventually raised doubts about the value of treating those who were not ill in areas where the infection rate was low or spotty. Here it was preferable to select for treatment only those heavily infected and in danger of ill health.

Unhappily, this new emphasis on worm burden threw a heavier weight than ever on the weak reed of sanitary toileting. Treatment could reduce heavy burdens to light ones. But a tidy avoidance of polluted soil, it was more obvious than ever, was the only way of breaking the chain of infection maintained by the "carriers"—persons with light infections.

The burden of the research lag rested even more heavily—if we may push the hookworm idiom this far—on Rose's doorstep after he hired Colonel Frederick F.

Russell (1870-1960) as Director of Public Health Laboratory Services. To strengthen state and local health services, Rose needed a man who could be loaned out to help organize good laboratories. What he had in mind, of course, was improvement of diagnostic services to doctors and patients, not research.

Russell, then fifty years old, was chief of the Army Surgeon General's Division of Infectious Diseases and Laboratories. He was already nationally known and honored. He joined the Army Medical Corps in the Spanish-American War and stayed on because the Army, at the turn of the century, offered him a career in laboratory medicine. The Surgeon General at that time was George Miller Sternberg (1838-1915), himself a laboratory scientist and justifiably known as the "Father of Bacteriology in America." Under Sternberg, the Army Medical Corps, with troops to take care of in the tropics of both hemispheres, pioneered in the development of preventive medicine, benefiting civilian populations as well as the soldiers stationed among them. Working at the Army Medical School in Washington between 1907 and 1913, Russell developed and introduced an antityphoid vaccine. When Darling went with the Foundation, Russell took his place in the Canal Zone and then went on to fight communicable diseases in the Army during World War I. The death rate from disease among American soldiers, which had been shockingly high in the war with Spain, was cut in half during World War I and Russell received much of the credit.

This giant of medical science (he was actually short, a bit stout, and friendly) was accustomed to walking with a military stride and a sure step. He came to work in January 1920, about the time Rose was pondering the limitations of hookworm knowledge and feeling a bit tormented by the word *eradication*. Russell's footfall was soon heard in many different places, including Rose's office. Russell moved rapidly from one state laboratory to another, and from one country to another—everybody wanted his advice—and meanwhile regularly popped in to see Rose and ask questions: about hookworm, malaria, and yellow fever. As he later related, he found Rose did not have the answers. No one knew the answers, for these were research questions. The gap that impressed Russell was not between scientific knowledge and its application but between what science knew and what it needed to know. But he did not find Rose eager to take the I.H.D. into field research, much less to be persuaded by Russell's tenet that every state laboratory should be doing *some* research in order to keep itself intellectually alive.

On the other hand, Rose had no objection to the International Health Division supporting other institutions in doing needed research. This, in a manner of speaking, enabled Russell to bring in through the back door the research emphasis that after 1928 was openly to dominate the International Health Division. At that door was the helminthologist William W. Cort and, from 1923 on, the pharmacologist, Paul D. Lamson, who as we have seen eventually worked on the vermifuge problem.

The Johns Hopkins School of Hygiene and Public Health had just opened its doors, in 1918. The school was giving post-graduate training to Rockefeller field directors, and to foreign doctors chosen for Foundation fellowships in public health.

In 1919 Cort became professor of helminthology. Cort had been in California as assistant professor of zoology in Berkeley, and investigated hookworm in California mines. He was impressed that attempts to control

hookworm disease had gone far beyond basic knowledge. On a field trip to Trinidad, he found I.H.D. doctors
hip-deep in soil pollution and other questions such as
how far can a hookworm larva crawl.

This idea of getting the professor out into the boon-
docks was the beginning of a Johns Hopkins–Rockefeller Foundation hookworm research relationship that
flourished for twenty or more years, outlasting the hookworm control program and placing Cort and his associates high among the world's experts on "Wormology."
One of his students was Dr. Norman R. Stoll, then per-
fecting a hookworm egg-counting technique that, after
1923, enabled hookworm doctors to estimate how many
worms a patient had from the number of hookworm
eggs in one gram of his feces.

In 1920, Cort outlined a joint research program and
presented it to Russell. Generally speaking what he proposed was field research in the form of research expeditions, more or less in the Darling manner but different
in that it would form a working relationship between
the academic and the world at large.

It took the great Dr. William H. Welch (1850-1934)
to sell this program to the Rockefeller Foundation.
Welch, the first dean of the Johns Hopkins Medical
School and the leader in putting American medical edu-
cation on a scientific base, was now the director of the
Johns Hopkins School of Public Health.

Welch and Simon Flexner, director of the Rockefeller Institute for Medical Research, were the outstanding physicians on the international health board of the
Foundation. Flexner had been Welch's student; they
were old friends, but they now found themselves opposed. Flexner played a familiar tune—the I.H.D. was
not a research organization. That was what the Institute

was for. Welch asked him if the Institute would do the research. Flexner said the Institute was not interested in hookworm. His position was untenable and Welch won the argument.

Russell quickly sold Rose on the new research program. Cort and his wormologists began a long series of laboratory and field studies that continued into the early 1940's. The Chinese study has been mentioned. Others lie beyond the scope of our story. The interplay of acquired immunity and nutritional balance in man's varying fortunes with hookworm disease was never finally resolved. Acquired immunity and antibodies could be demonstrated in dogs, but not in human beings. The ultimate opinion, still held, is that hookworm is a mild infection in persons who are well nourished and not deficient in iron. It is well known, of course, that the diets of many, if not most, native peoples in the moist tropics are poor both in quality and quantity. In Africa, for example, the worms are often found in children in combination with the protein deficiency disease, kwashiorkor (literally, "red boy").

In sum, the results of hookworm research fostered by the International Health Division from 1920 until its termination in 1951 was largely technical music, of great interest to the student but containing no lingering melody for the masses of barefooted, hookworm-infested humanity. Nobody came up with a soil disinfectant or vaccine to get the problem of prevention out of the dooryards and byways of people who dwelt amid their excreta, the captives of their own ignorance and poverty.

In 1923, Rose, then sixty-one, abdicated in favor of Russell. A change of direction seemed in order, and Rose helped engineer it himself. Frederick Gates came out of retirement to roar his disapproval at Rose, telling him, "There is nobody to take your place."

Nevertheless, to have to rethink and reorganize one's efforts for a new and different solution of a problem on which one has labored for thirteen years can be a suddenly tiring thought, suggesting the desirability of bringing in new blood. Therefore, Rose accepted the proposal that he succeed Buttrick as president of the General Education Board. He imposed one condition —that he be allowed to carry out his own idea for a new International Education Board that would seek to advance higher education and scientific research abroad, particularly in the fields of mathematics, physics, and chemistry. This was agreed. For some years, Rose had his own private philanthropy.

Rose recommended that Russell succeed him. The first question that Rose always asked about any candidate for his international health staff was "Does he have good judgment?" The I.H.D. was getting underway in programs to control malaria and yellow fever, and already running into tough scientific questions. The choice of Frederick Russell demonstrated Rose's good judgment. Russell was a medical research man, and research was what was needed. In due time, his own good judgment would be put to some severe tests.

A colleague once described Wickliffe Rose as "a mouselike man, self-effacing, but very clear about what he wanted to do." Intramural accounts of this forgotten hero of American public health tended to picture him as a somewhat unbelievable character, personally faultless, a quiet superman. Some closer observers, however, recognized him as a tense man who achieved outward self-control and mastery of his complex environment at a considerable expenditure of inner stress.

Having passed the age of sixty-five, Rose retired in 1928 from the General Education Board. In 1931, he was hiking up a hill on Vancouver Island, British Columbia, in pursuit of steelhead trout, when he suffered a fatal heart attack.

10

Hookworm Today

The hookworm doctors were realists sometimes to the point that they became mentally depressed. Realism compelled them in the 1930's to take stock of what they had accomplished in the American South since 1910.

The leader in this follow-up survey was Dr. Waller S. Leathers, one of Rose's fishing friends and by then head of the Department of Preventive Medicine and Public Health in the Vanderbilt School of Medicine. The first follow-up survey was made in Mississippi, in fifty-two "hookworm counties." The study showed that between 1910 and 1933 the incidence of hookworm infection in white persons in Mississippi had declined from 53.1 to 19.6 percent, a reduction of two thirds. The average number of worms per person had not been measurable in the old Sanitary Commission days, but in 1933 it fell in the light-infection class. This large reduction in incidence and, more importantly, probably in intensity had to be credited to public education to seek examination and treatment or other factors, because only about one in ten of the rural homes in 1933 had a satisfactory latrine.

In 1940, Alvin E. Keller and others summed up the results of studies of hookworm in eight Southern states. These were Alabama, Florida, Georgia, Kentucky, Mississippi, North Carolina, South Carolina, and Tennessee. Over all, they found that from the period 1910-1914 to 1930-1938, the average hookworm infection rate had declined from 37 to 11 percent. Only one in four of those infected could be considered to have clinical hookworm disease, on the basis of "moderate" to "very heavy" egg counts.

The conclusion was that the Rockefeller Sanitary Commission, followed by the International Health Division, "conducted one of the first important public health demonstrations in the United States," but "This disease has not yet been adequately controlled in many areas." Mainly these were the sandy coastal plains from North Carolina to Mississippi.

That was more than a quarter of a century ago. What is the situation in the South today?

In the first place, hookworm infection has not been eradicated, although hookworm *disease* is rarely seen. Dr. Henry P. Carr, who has written extensively on the disease, said that it still presents a "considerable problem" in some rural areas of his home state of Georgia. The same is true of Mississippi, Alabama, and some parts of other states. None of these rates the disease as more than a minor problem, however.

There has been no die-out effect in hookworm, as seen in successful attacks on some other diseases, for the worm continues to survive in the same areas that were centers of infestation fifty years ago. On the other hand, there has been a fade-out in both numbers of infections and intensity of infections in these areas, and something approaching a blank-out in the worms' damaging effects

to people's health. If control of disease, rather than eradication of the pathogen, is taken as the practical objective,
then the eventual result of the cooperative program of
the Rockefeller Sanitary Commission, the Rockefeller
Foundation, and state and local health departments must
be regarded as another example of success in disease conquest.

What has brought about the gradual disappearance
of hookworm disease—mainly an affliction of the poor
white—is a matter of speculation and some disagreement.
Certainly most would agree that the primary force in
tipping the scales against the worm was the education of
doctors to give and of patients to seek examination and
treatment for infection. The problem has been to hold
these gains through prevention of further contact with
polluted soil.

Sufficient earning capacity to buy shoes may have
played a part. Far more rural Southerners, children and
adults, now wear shoes in summer as well as winter.

The rural-urban population shift may have figured
in, by moving people who sought jobs in business or industry away from areas of heavy soil pollution and into
areas where sewer systems and indoor toilets were more
plentiful.

Economic prosperity, having greater impact on
the white man than the Negro, may be the most important factor, bringing purchasing power not only for
shoes but, more importantly, a diet containing sufficient
protein to provide resistance to the parasite.

One manifestation of economic and social progress
is rural electrification, not simply in the Tennessee Valley Authority area but throughout the South. A lag has
been observed between the introduction of electric
lights and of running water in rural homes, but the fact

remains that if electric power is available, water can be pumped and a flush toilet and septic tank can be installed if the householder can finance them. The rise of the flush toilet in the rural South appears so recently in the long-range trend, however, that it can be described only as a strong reinforcing factor in reducing hookworm.

In the absence of scientific studies of factors that have been effective against the hookworm in the American South, it would be not only safer but also sounder, probably, to conclude that effective hookworm control is the result of a variety of medical, public health, social, and economic efforts and circumstances that in combination have tipped the balance against the worm.

This is far from the case among the less fortunate peoples of other tropical or subtropical countries in the hookworm belt, where, Norman Stoll has estimated, more than 600 million are infected. In his view (1962), "the great campaign against it, which made such significant gains for public health, put little or no permanent crimp in hookworm outside of the southern United States."

Worldwide, the impact of hookworm infection upon health is hard to bring into focus, because of its tremendous geographic sprawl over three continents (Africa, Asia, and Latin America), because of the interplay of this disease with others, because of fragmentary reporting, and because of lack of public health interest in this disease. An excellent attempt to appraise the problem was made in *Tropical Health, a Report on a Study of Needs and Resources*, a study directed by Dr. Willard H. Wright and published by the National Academy of Sciences-National Research Council in 1962.

Hookworm ranked ninth in cases reported in 1957 for a survey population of 1.2 billion, behind yaws, influenza, tuberculosis, malaria, nutritional diseases, trachoma, bacillary dysentery, and pneumonia. It ranked twenty-third as a cause of death, in a list in which not a classical tropical disease but tuberculosis was at the top. (Tuberculosis takes a toll exceeding the next nine diseases combined—cholera, malaria, bacillary dysentery, pneumonia, smallpox, influenza, nutritional diseases, measles, and whooping cough.)

The world distribution of cases reported was Africa, 71 percent; South Central and Southeast Asia, 19 percent; the Caribbean, Central, and South America, 5 percent; Southwest Asia, 4 percent, and Oceania, 1 percent.

After a rather long lesson, over a sixty-year period, international health authorities are prone to be philosophical and look upon hookworm as ineradicable. As a matter of fact, they speak of roundworms, whipworms, and hookworms "as an index of socioeconomic status." Almost invariably the more advanced the community and the higher people stand in the community, the fewer worms there are to be found.

Whatever additional scientific knowledge of the worm is still needed, it would appear likely, as of today, that the hookworm problem occurs as a traveling companion of the food as much as the sanitation problem. Any great reduction of the disease in underdeveloped countries probably depends on a general improvement in nutrition. Whether this objective can be more easily accomplished than soil sanitation remains to be seen. The satisfaction of hunger, it must be granted, is a more compelling drive than the rather negative appeal for sanitary disposal of its waste products.

II

MALARIA—
NEW WORLDS AND
OLD MISERIES
TO CONQUER

11

Man versus Nature

In the tropical world, where the damp heat itself lies like a great weight on the land, malaria—nature's model of the torture rack—more than any other disease has made life, liberty, and the pursuit of happiness a weary, wearing business. One of civilization's least celebrated victories is the disappearance of malaria from the United States, Europe, and many parts of Latin America, and its progressive retreat, where systematically attacked, in India and other parts of Asia. The World Health Organization still regards malaria as public health enemy No. 1 in Africa south of the Sahara.

Malaria is as old as mankind. When human beings had toiled up the perilous paths of evolution and emerged on earth as such, mosquitoes were already on hand to sting them. We know this from the finding of mosquito fossils laid down in stone a hundred million years ago. Certain mosquitoes act as carriers of the malaria plasmodium, a microscopic one-celled protozoon, an undistinguished, ameba-like blob of plasma that, for its own survival, must attack red blood corpuscles of other animals.

Thus, the chills, fever, sweat, the swollen spleen, anemia, lack of vitality, and sometimes death from malaria seem to have been a legacy of human misery from the beginning of time. Scientists surmise this because animals much older than man in the scale of geological time —lizards, birds, monkeys, apes—suffer from mosquito bites and from malaria parasites of their own.

There are more than fifty species of malaria plasmodia, but only four primarily adapted to prey on man; the rest divide their attention among several hundred other vertebrate hosts. Many of the plasmodia of mammals depend on the anopheline genus of mosquitoes to carry them from host to host, but not exclusively, as is the case in human malaria. There are about 400 varieties of *Anopheles*, about sixty of them malaria carriers.

Malaria was well known to the "Father of Medicine," Hippocrates (460-377 B.C.), although it apparently was then a new disease in Greece. Hippocrates, as well as Chinese and Hindu physicians and priests before him, described the types of intermittent fever (malaria) as quotidian (daily), tertian (every other day), and quartan (every third day). He distinguished intermittent from the continuous fever more commonly observed in other infectious diseases.

Hippocrates identified enlargement of the spleen, a blood-regulating organ just under the ribs to the left of the stomach, with people who lived in low, damp, hot places and drank stagnant marsh water. A big spleen that the doctor can feel with his fingers has become a classic sign that a person has or recently has had malaria.

Medical historians believe that malaria, by sapping people's strength and depopulating the countryside, had a part in the downfall of Greek civilization. Eventually, the disease came to Rome, where the citizens began to write about intermittent fever some two hundred years after Hippocrates. People were advised against buying a farm or building a house in a swampy area. Of the many explanations of malaria, this one remained the most popular until the end of the nineteenth century—that swamps generated some kind of air-borne poison, a miasma.

Malaria means "bad air," and it is appropriate that the Italians, who have produced some of the best malariologists, should have named it. Though Edward Gibbon in his *Decline and Fall of the Roman Empire* completely scorned such a possibility, there are a few historians who believe that the "Roman airs," another name for malaria, contributed to the failure of the Roman, as well as the Greek, way of life. If this is true, then it is certainly possible to believe that bloodthirsty plasmodia have done as much to determine the ebb and flow of human society as the most violent and destructive of the emperors and tyrants. These men are puny characters, indeed, beside protozoa that, as late as twenty years ago, were killing as many as three million persons a year. What other would-be dictator of human destiny could make this claim—to have made ecological puppets of the Caesars, to have invaded the Vatican and killed popes and cardinals, to have helped drive the Spanish and French imperialists out of the West Indies, to have made mosquito preserves of some of the world's richest lands?

There was a sense of humor in the way Chinese mythology described the three malaria demons—one had a hammer, another a pail of water, and the third a stove, thus providing for the headache, chills, and fever. This is the way of malaria. The chill, taking place while the body's temperature is rising, may shake the bed. The fever sometimes peaks at 106° to 107° and may end in one hour or last a day or more. The bout is then over, and the patient gets up, only to be felled again twelve to sixty hours later. Eventually the infection runs its course and subsides. An individual's chance of dying of malaria depends on many factors, including the type and strain of plasmodia attacking his blood. Certain strains of the falciparum type are extremely dangerous. Malaria of the vivax type is a debilitating disease of great morbidity and low mortality. Yet, like influenza, any malaria can kill tremendous numbers because it strikes so many.

During a malaria bout, a patient acquires some immunity. But the resistance is not as solid or as lasting as in some diseases caused by bacteria or viruses. In the course of more or less continuous exposure to infected mosquitoes night after night, the Negroes of Africa develop a great tolerance for vivax malaria, not so much for falciparum. They achieve their resistance over a period of years, and at the cost of death to many babies and small children who succumb before they build an immunity. There is no effective vaccine against malaria.

Freedom from malaria sounds simple, theoretically. All that is necessary is to avoid being bitten by the night-feeding female of certain anopheline mosquitoes, at a time when this female a fortnight or so before has sucked the blood of some person whose malaria spores were ready to migrate. It has taken the human mind thousands of years, however, to get to understand malaria well enough to know how to avoid it—to realize, for example, that human blood and not swamp water is the reservoir of malaria.

Few living creatures have developed a more uncertain survival method than malaria plasmodia. For example, consider this: male adult mosquitoes feed on plant juices, but the female, having a sharper beak, can draw blood; in fact, after mating, she usually requires a "blood meal," as the scientists call it, to develop her eggs. The plasmodium depends on the female's taste for blood to find new blood streams where it can spawn!

The death rate of mosquitoes is high from hatching on; most mosquitoes live only a few days or weeks; some live several months; a few survive the winter in cold climates. Thus, the chain of infection would appear easy to break. One factor works on the plasmodium's side, however; malaria patients may remain infected and be recurrently infectious for two or three years. The future of plasmodia consequently depends on the probability that through the large numbers of people with active malaria, of mosquitoes, and of mosquito bites, the one-to-one chain will remain unbroken and at times become greater than one to one when many mosquitoes bite one malaria patient.

The person whose knowledge of mosquitoes is confined to the pest types, such as *Culex pipiens*, might think this would be hard to do—for several mosquitoes to tap the patient's blood stream. It is not. The *Culex* gives herself away with an annoying hum and by causing pain at the moment of inserting her beak; itching and swelling follow. But the mosquito selected by the plasmodium as its vehicle is not that inept; the insidious anopheline approaches silently and disturbs its host very little with pain or itching. In fact, its saliva is believed to have anesthetic properties.

Thus, the malaria parasite has been a great biological success, relying on a principle by which all living things routinely accomplish their purpose: the saturation of numbers favors any given chance. To avoid extinction, the parasite produces hundreds of spores; the mosquito in turn lays hundreds of eggs. Most of the offspring of both are killed, but some survive and keep busy. *Overcreation* is nature's way of feeding her entire flock and assuring each species of survival.

All this sets the stage, so to speak, for a tiny band of Scots, Italians, Americans, and one Frenchman who, at the end of the nineteenth century, fell to work filling in the fantastically complicated details of the simple equation that man plus mosquito equals malaria—sometimes. Sometimes it is yellow fever or dengue fever or filariasis. Most of the time it equals no more than a mosquito bite.

The modern scientific story of malaria began with Charles Louis Alphonse Laveran (1845-1922). Examining under the microscope the fresh blood of a malaria patient in Algeria, Laveran, a French army surgeon, in 1880 saw on his glass slide a spherical body with red pigment in it suddenly put out little whiplike hairs, or flagella. What he had observed we now know was the male form (gametocyte) of the malaria plasmodium in the first stage of sexual reproduction; the flagella seek the female gametocyte and fertilize it so that it can spore within the mosquito.

The medical profession remained thoroughly skeptical of Laveran's finding until 1886, when Camillo Golgi (1844-1926), an Italian physician, confirmed it. Golgi also observed the plasmodium in a second, nonsexual stage of multiplication, wherein it splits and releases new spores in the patient's blood stream. This stage, he showed, coincided with the paroxysm, or chills soon followed by fever. At this time, there may be millions of spores in circulation.

Cinchona bark and finally the pure derivative, quinine, having been the specific treatment for malaria over the previous three hundred years, discovery of the specific cause of the disease was really "useless knowledge" until identification of its insect carrier. There was nothing one could do about malaria except take quinine.

Various astute observers had suspected the mosquito, mentioned as a malaria carrier in Sanskrit literature at least 1,500 years old. It took the general discovery that insects can carry other diseases to bring the mosquito theory of malaria infection to scientific test. This knowledge evolved in the ten or fifteen years before 1895. Doctor (later Sir) Patrick Manson (1844-1922) found the threadlike worm of filariasis growing in the stomachs of mosquitoes that had fed on the blood of patients with this disease. Others found that ticks and tsetse flies carried diseases of cattle and horses.

"Mosquito" Manson, whom fellow London doctors regarded as a crackpot, theorized that mosquitoes were not merely carriers of malaria but acted as intermediate hosts during a stage in which the parasite reproduced and developed in preparation to be spread back to the human host. This was, to repeat, a sexual stage. Manson could not prove this; what he claimed sounded both fuzzy and farfetched. It led, for example, to the question of whether infected mosquitoes get chills and fever. There is, as a matter of fact, no evidence that the parasite harms its insect host in the least.

Manson showed "Laveran's bodies" to Ronald Ross (1857-1932), a British army surgeon, who had not been able to distinguish the plasmodia himself. In 1895, Ross returned to India and set out to test Manson's theory. Was the mosquito host for a distinct stage in the life cycle of the plasmodium, as had been observed with certain other parasites? Was it as impossible for the parasite to get along without mosquitoes as without human beings?

The answer, Ross proved, was "Yes." The parasite was obligated to both of these hosts for its survival. Ross began by raising *Culex* and *Aëdes* mosquitoes from larvae and fed them on patients with malaria. He then dissected the mosquito's stomach—an elementary detail for the modern malariologist but Ross had to work out the technique for himself by placing the mosquito under a microscope and using needles as cutting tools. He saw the malaria gametocytes put out their flagella, but nothing further. He then put malarious mosquitoes in water to die, and had healthy volunteers drink the water. The first volunteer coincidentally came down with malaria, but the next twenty-one subjects did not, thus disposing of the old idea of Hippocrates, accepted by Manson, that drinking water was the route of infection.

Next, Ross caused *Culex* and *Aëdes* mosquitoes to feed on malaria patients and then a few days later bite healthy volunteers. No one got malaria.

Ross was no entomologist. He did not know there was such a thing as a spotted-winged *Anopheles* mosquito until he saw one in the hills near Ootacamund, in the province of Madras. He wondered if he had perhaps been using the wrong mosquito.

This was the turning point.

In 1897, in Secunderbad, he saw what happened when this mosquito imbibed malarious blood. He saw cysts growing in the mosquito's stomach wall; these cysts contained pigmented malaria parasites.

This discovery inspired him to write a poem in a letter to his wife, saying he had found "thy cunning seeds, O million murdering Death." Switching to bird malaria—the malaria peculiar to birds—as a more convenient research tool, Ross now showed that these seeds, emerging from ruptured cysts as rodlike spores, collected in the mosquito's salivary glands, and were secreted in saliva that wetted the insect's proboscis as it jabbed it into a host's blood capillary.

"Never in our dreams had we imagined such a wonderful tale as this," he later wrote. By 1898, he had demonstrated the entire life cycle of the parasite in bird malaria. In the same year, an Italian group headed by Giovanni Battista Grassi (1854-1925) clinched the case against anopheline mosquitoes as the only offender in transmission among humans. In 1899, now in Sierra Leone, Ross completed his story on the plasmodium's life cycle in human malaria. Such research as remained to be done he called "a work for children."

At any rate, the Dark Age of Ignorance on malaria was over. Ross was knighted and received the Nobel Prize in 1902. Laveran received it in 1907. Golgi got it, too, in 1906, not for his classic malaria work but for developing a staining method that enabled him to reveal the structure of brain and other nerve cells.

The new target for attack was the female anopheline mosquito that spawned the seeds of malaria and injected them with its proboscis. Between 1899 and 1902, Ross himself demonstrated the classic methods of mosquito control—drainage of the soil, oiling of stagnant pools, screening of buildings, isolation of persons with malaria, and the regular use of mosquito nets over beds.

12

"More Dangerous than the Crocodile"

Wickliffe Rose returned from his trip around the world in 1914 ready to admit that malaria, not hookworm, was the tropical world's worst health problem. He was impressed with what he learned from Sir Ronald Ross in London and Sir Malcolm Watson (1873-1955) in Malaya.

Rose found Ross much exasperated at the world's failure to exploit his discovery that the mosquito was to blame for malaria. "I didn't do this work on malaria in the interests of zoology," he told Rose, "but in the interest of practical sanitation." For the most part, the medical profession was still pursuing malaria with quinine. Although theoretically, if every case of malaria were cured with quinine, there would be no plasmodia left for the mosquitoes to transmit, Ross had no faith in that approach. Rose could sympathize with him; eradication through treatment was presenting the same problem in hookworm disease.

Ross's central proposition to Rose was for the International Health Division to put on a demonstration in some malaria hotspot to show beyond any further doubt that malaria could be completely eradicated through mosquito control. If Rose needed any further convincing, he should look up Malcolm Watson when he was in the Malay States. As Ross said, with his usual poetic flourish: "Watson is my Elisha, who 'took the mantle of Elijah that fell from him, and smote the waters.' "

Rose, touring the rubber and coconut estates from Renang to Singapore, found "Elisha" in Klang, where Watson was responsible for the health of the Tamil and Chinese coolies on a large number of plantations. When he came to Klang in 1901, Watson was innocent of all knowledge of malaria or mosquitoes, but now he knew that "*Anopheles* is more dangerous than the crocodile, king cobra, or tiger." He arrived in an epidemic year, when the Klang yearly death rate was 368 per thousand. It was now down to 45.

Watson's primary point of attack was permanent drainage, through open ditch and subsoil tile pipe. The change in the Indians' health had been spectacular. They usually came from the lowest castes and famine areas of India, arriving in rags, half-starved, and infected with hookworm. A year on a healthy estate improved a Tamil and his family beyond recognition; he could save money with the hope of returning home when conditions there improved. On a malarious estate, however, he and his family were doomed. A great complication of malaria is that it may cause the pregnant woman to abort. One plantation employed an average of fifty Tamil women, and yet over a six-year period not one woman bore a living child, despite special food and care and the offer of a prize to the first to deliver a healthy child. Children were now being born on this estate.

Rose had known malaria in Tennessee, but nothing like this. Watson assured him it was a far greater problem in Malaya than hookworm, although the latter was widely prevalent. Rose was impressed that the estate managers considered the cost of Malayan malaria control was an excellent investment in labor efficiency.

Watson recently had visited the Panama Canal and spoke in glowing terms of William C. Gorgas (1854-1920), a United States Army physician. Watson called Gorgas's control of yellow fever and malaria in the Canal Zone "the greatest sanitary achievement the world has ever seen." Gorgas impressed Watson because, as Watson later said, "the man who acts as a link between discovery and its application needs a combination of qualities as rare as those of the pure investigator." General Gorgas was, of course, a familiar figure. He had been elected a commissioner of the International Health Division at its first meeting in 1913.

Because of the international attention focused on the Panama Canal during its construction from 1904 to 1914, Gorgas more than Ross or Watson was the one who put mosquito control on the map. His combined methods, introduced in 1901, following the Spanish-American War, brought malaria in Havana almost to the point of disappearance; malaria incidence in that city dropped from 901 cases per thousand population in 1899 to 19 in 1908.

Gorgas paid a great deal of attention to the larvae hatching from eggs that the *Anopheles* mosquitoes laid in the stagnant waters of swamps, ponds, and puddles near dwellings in Havana. By spraying these waters with kerosene or crude oil, his engineers and their crews made it impossible for the larvae to mature, since they could not come to the surface to breathe. Gorgas threw the book at them—drainage, brush and grass cutting, oiling, other larvicides, quinine given preventively, screening, and the killing of mosquitoes in houses by insecticide fumigation.

Gorgas and his Sanitary Department greatly reduced malaria in the Canal Zone with the same methods, but encountered difficulties. Here, it was more of a rural—in fact, jungle—disease than in the city of Havana. The costs, though essential to canal construction, were high.

Eventually, history recognized that Gorgas, one of public health's greatest field generals, made the Canal possible by completely controlling yellow fever and almost but not quite wiping out malaria, two diseases that had made the Isthmus of Panama previously a graveyard for foreigners, from early pirates to French canal builders.

For the moment, the Gorgas record in Rose's mind neatly bracketed the dilemma of malaria control. Granted he had proved that *malaria could be prevented, but could it be done at a cost ordinary civilian communities could afford?*

Rose found one other source of encouragement: the United States Public Health Service, whose officers, Drs. Henry Rose Carter (1852-1925), and Rudolph H. von Ezdorf (1872-1916), had become excited about the possibility of duplicating the Panama Canal success in the southern United States.

They began in 1912 with a postcard survey of physicians in twelve states to determine how many malaria cases they saw. The number per year was estimated to be one million. The death rate was not generally high, because the malaria was mostly vivax. In some parts of the South there was no malaria at all. In the low coastal plains, however, malaria lay over the land like a great pall, dragging the tenant farmer and his family down, precipitating the abandonment of farms, slowing the wheels of the cotton mills.

13

The Malarious South

The first controlled experiment in malaria prevention in the United States was conducted in the neighborhood of a large cotton mill at Roanoke, North Carolina, where the manager was running so short of labor due to malaria in 1913 that he called on the Public Health Service for help. Anti-mosquito measures solved his problem. Again, in 1914, an appeal came from a physician for a lumber mill at Electric Mills, Mississippi. There, too, Public Health Service physicians and sanitary engineers attacked the mosquito and got results.

Federal support for these first efforts was $16,000 appropriated by Congress in 1914 in response to Carter's and von Ezdorf's testimony, the first government appropriation for malaria control. In 1915 and 1916, similar projects were undertaken in Alabama and Virginia.

In his annual report for 1915, Rose pointed out that malaria impaired economic efficiency, retarded physical and mental development, and had wide geographical distribution, in some regions being "responsible for more sickness and death than all other diseases combined." It was the "most serious medical and sanitary problem with which we have to contend," he said.

The Rockefeller Foundation ventured into malaria control cautiously, in contrast to its forthright crusade against hookworm disease. Even so, its first appropriation for a malaria control demonstration, $30,000 in 1915, was nearly twice Congress's first appropriation.

Following his policy of not going anywhere he wasn't invited, Rose first had sought the advice of Surgeon General Rupert Blue, who suggested that the International Health Division join forces with the Public Health Service and the state and local health departments in three demonstrations in Arkansas. Rose drew up a world survey of malaria and coordinated it with Blue before obtaining the approval of his own Board. It was the beginning of a long, happy friendship between a government and a voluntary health agency.

The I. H. D.'s first adventure, in what Rose termed "frankly an experiment," took place in Bolivar County, Mississippi, beginning in July 1915. The project was under the direction of Dr. Waller S. Leathers and Dr. Charles C. Bass. Both were old Rockefeller Sanitary Commission friends. The big idea here was to determine what could be accomplished with quinine alone and, in so doing, standardize the dosage, customarily taken hit or miss as prescribed by doctors or in various patent medicine "chill tonics."

Bass, first in Bolivar and then in Sunflower County, showed that by administering ten grains of quinine a day for eight weeks it was possible to kill the parasites in the blood of about 90 percent of all cases treated. This became known as the "Bass treatment." He had begun, of course, by trying to find every case of old or new malaria in the study area, as shown by blood examination or history of an attack in the past year. Quinine was provided free. Overall, the incidence of malaria was reduced about 50 percent in three years' time at an annual cost ranging from 38 cents to $1.09 per capita. One happy consequence of the standardization of dosage was to make quinine available in Southern drug stores for about half the previous price.

Crossett, Arkansas, a lumber town of 2,129 inhabitants in 1916, was the scene of the first Public Health Service–Rockefeller Foundation cooperative project. Malaria comprised 60 percent of the illness seen by local physicians. The objective was to learn what could be accomplished by various simple measures—by draining or filling borrow pits and shallow ponds, clearing underbrush to let sunlight reach streams, cleaning their shallows of vegetation and obstruction, getting rid of artificial water containers around houses, and weekly spraying of all remaining breeding places with road oil. The idea was to make it difficult for the mosquitoes to lay their eggs, for the eggs to hatch, and for the larvae finally to develop as adult mosquitoes.

The results startled the community. In the malarious Old South, chills and fever would appear soon after the first mosquitoes, around May, and with them reach a peak in September and October, not dropping off until after the first cold snap. In 1916, however, the Crossett people noticed that they were not being bothered by mosquitoes. By the end of the year, their doctors were complaining about vanishing income. The number of calls the doctors received to see patients with malaria dropped from 2,100 in the last six months of 1915 to 310 in the same period of 1916. Meanwhile, the malaria parasite index in residents examined dropped 72 percent in the first six months. The cost was 50 to 60 cents per capita after the first year. The story was much the same in Lakeville and Hamburg.

The experiments were a smash hit. It is seldom that anything a public health doctor does to prevent disease can be quickly measured in loss of business for practicing doctors attending the sick, but this can happen with malaria. Furthermore, it cost less to fight mosquitoes than pay the doctors' bills for malaria.

During World War I the Public Health Service and Army successfully employed the same combined methods to prevent malaria in and around military training camps and key industrial centers. These efforts ended with the war.

The International Health Division by 1919 was ready to accept malaria control as part of its mission. The following year it entered an arrangement with the Public Health Service and state departments of health to do joint malaria control demonstrations in fifty-two towns in ten states. This new endeavor was launched in the midst of a severe economic depression in the South; thus the results were even more attractive. At an average cost of 78 cents a person, malaria in these fifty-two communities was reduced anywhere from 30 to 98 percent in 1920. As state and local funds increased, malaria control became a part of regular county health programs.

The I. H. D. malaria staff, numbering about a dozen and a half, at first confined itself to towns. To go out into the country and control *Anopheles* had seemed an uninviting prospect. However, a three-year experiment beginning in 1918 in Hinds County, Mississippi, showed that by attacking mosquito breeding places for a quarter mile around each house the incidence of malaria could be reduced 77 percent at a cost of from $2.60 to $3.09 per capita. Two methods were used, oiling the surfaces of stagnant waters and distributing top minnows. The big problem was the cost.

The enlistment of surface-feeding fish to eat mosquito larvae in malarious ponds was a clever but not new idea. This biological method was both a useful and appealing idea, turning nature against herself, as it were. The American fish best suited to the job was the top minnow (*Gambusia affinis*); it was easily transported, multiplied rapidly, wintered well, and had a voracious appetite for mosquitoes' eggs and larvae. The top minnows were cheaper than oil, involved little labor, only occasionally required restocking, and could be used in mosquito breeding places where oil was out of the question, such as stock ponds and pasture creeks. In Hinds County, 80 to 90 percent of the water surfaces were controlled with top minnows alone.

Rose, describing everything that had been done in malaria control until that time as "nibbling efforts," in 1921 announced a major attack on the disease "along the entire front, including town, village, and open country." Malaria problems were attacked as far north and west as Missouri, Illinois, and California, and by 1923 the program was operating in more than 160 counties, fifteen states, and seven foreign countries (Brazil, Ecuador, Italy, Nicaragua, Palestine, Philippine Islands, and Puerto Rico).

Two truisms of malaria control were now fairly apparent: 1. No matter what tried and true method of mosquito control you choose, if you use it systematically, malaria, when thus pushed, recedes. 2. Relaxation tends to follow intensive effort and so, when the pushing stops, malaria tends to come back. Then the whole story starts over again. This is the dull part of public health.

The malaria is much the same as the hookworm

story in one respect: The more the malaria control team
—the public health administrator, the malariologist, the
sanitary engineer, and the entomologist—piled up experience, the more questions popped up. Malaria research
had advanced little since Ross was in the field twenty
years before; the only thing new, of practical significance, was that in 1921 two Rockefeller men, Marshall
Barber (1868-1953) and Theodore B. Haynes (1898-
1930), on a tip from someone in New Orleans, carried out
some experiments with Paris green and found that this
copper-arsenic dust was far superior to oil or anything
else as a malaria mosquito larvicide. It could be sprayed
over calm or slowly moving water surfaces by hand,
blower, or airplane. The Foundation was the first big customer for Paris green, a stomach poison cheaply manufac-
turable by the ton. The stuff soon became the backbone
of mosquito control and remained so until World War
II. The amount floating on the water proved harmless to
animals and fish.

Such shotgun methods had weaknesses as well as
strengths. In favor of them, one county health officer
said, "The average layman, while willing to accept the
mosquito-borne theory, thinks you are splitting hairs too
much in laying all the blame on one species of the family.
As long as you have mosquitoes puncturing the hide of
the average farmer you are going to do very little work
in malaria control unless you go after the whole tribe."
To increase hits and reduce costs, nevertheless, the scientist needed to be specific about his target. Anopheline
mosquitoes are the carriers of the plasmodium. There
were three species in the eastern United States, *Anopheles quadrimaculatus, A. crucians,* and *A. punctipennis.* Carter said quadrimaculatus was the only important
malaria carrier in the Southern United States. If true,

what were the breeding, feeding, resting, and flight habits that would distinguish the "quad" from the others? To waste time and money killing nonmalarial mosquitoes would in the long run doom the program to discredit and defeat, no matter what the average farmer wanted.

Rose, the public health administrator who had set out to close the gap between existing knowledge and its application, understood the point continually being made by Frederick Russell, the medical scientist, who succeeded him. Field research was as necessary in malaria as in hookworm disease. Rose, not long before his retirement in 1923, called on Dr. Samuel T. Darling to set up a malaria control training station and research laboratory in Leesburg, Georgia.

Darling soon confirmed Carter's observation. *A. quadrimaculatus* carried all the human malaria in Georgia. Studies at Johns Hopkins showed why. Crucians and punctipennis preferred to feed on animals, whereas quadrimaculatus favored humans; it bred in the still waters of the lowlands, whereas punctipennis was a hill-stream mosquito. Crucians bred side by side with the "quads."

To Leesburg came Dr. Paul F. Russell, the young Bostonian who went to Cornell and foreswore becoming a medical missionary to join the Rockefeller Foundation staff. Darling asked Russell if he could determine any differences among the larvae of the three species of anopheline mosquitoes. The adults were easily distinguished, but nobody could tell the wigglers apart. Russell counted hairs on 1,000 larvae and found there were species differences in the position and character of the hairs. He then produced a key for identification of *A. quadrimaculatus*, the one logical candidate for Paris green.

The Leesburg research also exploded a common fallacy, and one that still persists, derived from observations of anophelines abroad. It is that this mosquito, the carrier of malaria, always "stands on its head," meaning that its body angles upward rather than running parallel to its resting surface, as does *Culex*, the pest. The fact is that *A. quadrimaculatus* assumes a position not too different from *Culex*, whereas *A. crucians* and *A. punctipennis*, the innocent ones, have the rocket-launching stance.

Knowledge of such details sharpened the attack, and Paris green provided a more effective punch against the quadrimaculatus larvae in the mill ponds and lime sinks of the South. By 1927, Frederick Russell was able to state, quite correctly, "Malaria has practically disappeared from the cities and towns of the republic." Rural malaria, on the other hand, remained a troublemaker for another twenty years.

14

Italian Mosquitoes Don't Behave Right

Italian mosquitoes were different from American ones. This fact remained to be discovered when Lewis H. Hackett (1884-1962) arrived on the scene in 1923. A Californian, he had obtained the first doctor-of-public-health degree awarded by Harvard University, in 1913. What happened in the next seven years established the pivotal importance of entomology in malariology; the entomologists had a lot to learn, too.

Epidemic malaria was one of the costs of World War I. The British, French, and German armies, whose medical officers scoffed at the warnings of Ross and Laveran, were reduced to vast sick and convalescent camps in Macedonia for three years. Ordered to attack, a French general replied that he couldn't because his army was in the hospital with malaria. Both troops and refugees carried malaria throughout southern Europe and the Near East and eventually into northern Europe. Russia had one of the most terrible epidemics of malaria in modern times, with an estimated 18 million cases in 1923 and death rates in some places reaching 40 percent.

Italians were coming down with malaria at the rate

of about 2 million cases a year when Rose, in early 1922, received an invitation from health officials in Italy to visit the country and discuss the problem. Later that year, Benito Mussolini took over the government and became dictator. Whatever else may be said of Mussolini —from a humanitarian standpoint it is not much—he liked efficiency, whether in health, agriculture, or in making the trains run on time. At the invitation of the Italian National Health Department, Rose sent Hackett from Brazil to Italy to work with already distinguished Italian malaria scientists.

The Volscians (marsh dwellers) once farmed the region known as the Pontine Marshes. The Romans destroyed their towns. Attempts to recolonize the marshes failed because of malaria. Much the same thing happened along the coast of Italy from Rome to Pisa, once thickly populated but devastated by the Goths and Saracens and finally by the feudal armies of Pisa and Siena. They left the malaria mosquitoes in full possession. As Hackett pointed out, the Italian farmers are great colonizers, and yet they did not prosper even in the circle of cultivable Campagna around their capital city.

Not that they didn't try. The artificial drainage of this plain is a practice older than Roman civilization. The Etruscans previously faced the problem of *tufo terroso*, the rock stratum underlying some top soils of the Campagna. The *tufo* kept surface waters from seeping downward, interfered with soil fertility, and formed pools and marshes that were identified as the source of the "Roman airs." Roman hydraulic engineers, elaborating on the efforts of the Etruscans, built water tunnels that served many purposes through the centuries—mosquito control, irrigation, drinking water, storm drains, and sewage disposal. Rulers from the Caesars to Mussolini fussed over these drains, and through drainage, sought land reclamation, or bonification, as Italians call it. Thus far, these people had won some battles, but malaria had won the campaign.

The Italian malariologists were at the time inclined to regard Ross's man-mosquito-man theory of malaria transmission as simple-minded, even though Gorgas and Watson had proved the mosquito to be the key of malaria control in Panama and Malaya. There were in fact some European sanitarians who openly pooh-poohed Gorgas's hard work in the Canal Zone. These critics argued that the French canal builders had the bad luck to arrive in Panama during a cycle of climatic, water table, and soil conditions favorable to epidemics. The Americans, on the other hand, had the good fortune to arrive during a period of rapid decline in mosquito-borne diseases. In other words, the whole thing could be explained as a double coincidence!

The Italians, for whom Hackett became the English-language spokesman, did not question that anopheline mosquitoes carry malaria, but were sure there was something more to it—a factor *x*, they called it. As a German entomologist, Erich Martini (1880-1960), agreed, "A simple explanation of a natural phenomenon is probably wrong."

A hardy, versatile species, *Anopheles maculipennis*, had been identified as the main vector of malaria in Europe. In contrast to *A. quadrimaculatus* in America, this European mosquito and malaria did not necessarily come and go together. Sometimes there were many mosquitoes in the houses of southern Europe and little malaria; sometimes there was much malaria and few mosquitoes. The Italians refined the problem even further: Malaria was supposed to be a swamp disease, but they pointed out that there were swamps without malaria and malaria without swamps.

This was the mystery that Hackett faced with his Italian colleagues, especially Dr. Alberto Missiroli (1883-1951), the Italian government's No. 1 malariologist.

They soon answered one question. Whereas quadrimaculatus in America fled from water in motion, maculipennis in Italy could breed in swamps or drainage ditches. This explained why open drainage failed in Italy while succeeding in America and Malaya.

Malariologists, beginning with Watson, for some years had emphasized the necessity of a rifle-shot, rather than a shotgun, approach. This gave birth to "species sanitation" and finally "species eradication." For example, though *A. quadrimaculatus* was almost the sole malaria carrier in the eastern United States, it was *A. minimus flavirostris* in the Philippines, *A. pseudopunctipennis* in Argentina, and *A. gambiae* in tropical Africa. Each species has different habits. Some breed in salt water, some in fresh water, some like it standing; some like it running; some seek shady places and others like the sun. The variations seem endless.

The European *A. maculipennis*, a domestic mosquito that spends most of its adult life under a roof, going outdoors only to mate or lay eggs, was thought to be all one species until Missiroli, Hackett, and Martini put their minds to it. Others had turned up a miscellany of discrepancies in maculipennis. One scientist accounted for the absence of malaria despite the presence of mosquitoes by observing that domestic animals, stabled near the house, seemed to attract them away from man. Another noticed that some of the same mosquitoes in Holland did not hibernate in the winter, whereas most did. Still another noticed some with shorter wings.

Another Italian noted that maculipennis laid various types of eggs; he divided them into two classes, dark and gray, and called them messeae and labranchiae in honor of friends in the Health Department, Doctors Messea and Labranca. Another noticed variations in the number of "teeth" along the proboscis, and decided that mosquitoes with more teeth were so designed to cut through thick cow or horse hides and satisfy their taste for animal blood.

In 1930, Missiroli and Hackett examined the blood in the stomachs of maculipennis mosquitoes found in houses and discovered it often was of animal, rather than human, origin. These mosquitoes had flown in from the stables. This showed one could not determine the feeding preference of mosquitoes from the place of capture. Indeed, mosquitoes that had been sampling human blood could be found in the stables. The malariologists established that the amount of malaria in a locality was not in proportion to the total number of maculipennis mosquitoes there, but to the number of those that were "man eaters." Some definitely were not, and this bore no relation to their number of teeth.

In the next year, the story was complete. So-called maculipennis was not a single species but a complex of six subspecies that looked alike, except for those with the short wings. All could be told apart only from their eggs, variously barred or dappled. The six types were labranchiae, the most common malaria carrier, and elutus, also a dangerous customer; typicus, melanoon, and messeae, which preferred to feed on animals and seldom carried malaria, and atroparvus, which was less discriminating and therefore a possible source of malaria.

These look-alike mosquitoes behaved in remarkably different ways. Some bred in the coastal marshes, others in river valleys, and still others in little pools along mountain streams. Therefore, it was possible for a community to have malaria even when drought had dried up the swamps.

European malariologists, sharply skeptical, retraced and confirmed the Italian-American-German group's observations and they then plunged into a fantastically detailed elaboration of the facts about the maculipennis complex. It bore out Martini's remark that nothing is simple in nature. Nevertheless, the factor x had been found.

While Hackett thoroughly enjoyed the scholarly approach, and exhibited both scientific and literary talent, he was in Italy to control malaria. Hence, he had begun— in collaboration with the National Health Department— by establishing a Malaria Experimental Station in a small, beautiful palace in Rome. Dr. Missiroli was chosen to direct it. Together, they picked a town, Portotorres, in Sardinia, for the first experiment in Europe with the new larvicide, Paris green. Hackett was clever about it. He said he would not spend more than the inhabitants had spent in the previous year on quinine.

It was another triumph, à la Gorgas. From 1924 to 1929 the Hackett team drove the Portotorres spleen index, blood parasite index, chronic malaria case rate, infant infection rate, and mosquito catch from the former high peaks almost, but not quite, down to zero. They then held these rates at a minimum for another four years. It was all done simply by poisoning *A. maculipennis labranchiae* larvae with Paris green in their natural breeding spots.

Missiroli-directed Paris green experiments now blossomed all over Italy. The only trouble was that a few

European malaria experts did not believe what was happening, even when they read the scientific reports on Portotorres and visited the town, and even when the work was duplicated in other Italian towns. As a matter of fact, malaria control methods became an all-around subject of controversy as the result of a series of surveys by a newly formed Malaria Commission of the League of Nations Health Organization. Following the death of Darling, the Commission for some time lacked American representation and its eight experts included no one with successful experience in controlling malaria mosquitoes.

In 1927, the Malaria Commission upset the Americans by publishing a report that charged the treatment of malaria with quinine was being neglected in favor of antilarval measures. The Commission said that knowledge of the mosquito transmission of malaria did not help in the struggle against the disease, and in fact led away from the right path, for it was a social disease that responded to general improvement of conditions of living.

To make matters worse, the Commission sent two of its members to the United States for a malaria control survey. They reported that malaria was receding in the United States at a constant rate from north to south and that the trend had begun long before the public health attack began. They assigned the great reduction of malaria in the United States to general agricultural drainage, the disappearance of mill ponds, screening, and the Bass standard treatment with quinine. Neither was impressed with mosquito eradication projects as such. The outraged American reaction to their mimeographed report gave the League Health Organization second thoughts, and it did not publish it.

The Commission did, however, hold out one provocative idea. This was to enlist the cooperation of the malarious people themselves in killing mosquitoes found gorged with blood on their bedroom walls. Here was the moment at which mosquitoes became malaria carriers, and therefore the most logical point of attack; killing mosquito larvae was pretty far off the mark, it was argued, inasmuch as only a few mosquitoes lived long enough or traveled far enough to bite a person with malaria.

Practical public health men, and particularly the larviciders, scratched their heads peevishly and muttered: "True, true, but how do you get uneducated, unintelligent people to do this?" If they had learned anything, it was that the routine voluntary cooperation of human beings was a reed too weak to support the weight of mass disease prevention.

They, in turn, slighted another development. This was the use of pyrethrum, from a daisy-like chrysanthemum growing in Dalmatia, as a household spray. This deadly insecticide is so old that mention of it can be found in *Arabian Nights*. Its use against flies and mosquitoes had grown until in the 1920's the United States was using millions of pounds of pyrethrum. Dissolved in kerosene, it became the base of the spray used in Flit guns throughout America and, eventually, went into the aerosol "bombs" used by the Army Air Forces against insects in World War II. G. A. Park Ross was the first to use it as a house spray against malaria in South Africa, beginning in 1930. The spray had to be used intelligently and regularly, but it controlled malaria.

To finish the pyrethrum research story, presaging still greater things to come: Paul Russell, Frederick W. Knipe, and T. R. Rao of India in the middle 1930's tested the periodic spraying of houses in south India and found the methods highly effective against malaria transmitted by *Anopheles culicifacies*. The villagers welcomed pyrethrum. Said Russell: "I had been forced to conclude that no measure of malaria control had been demonstrated that was economically feasible for rural India. . . . Now we had a method that would completely stop the transmission of malaria in certain rural tropical areas, at a cost of less than ten cents per capita per year."

The I. H. D. concluded in 1934 that the experimental phase of antilarval control of malaria was over. The Paris green method was in wide use throughout Italy and other parts of Europe. During the previous year the spotted wings of maculipennis were not seen in towns so treated, and malaria in Portotorres was down 90 percent from 1924. The I. H. D. terminated the Malaria Experimental Station in Rome, Missiroli became director of a malaria division of the government Institute of Public Health, and his friend Hackett turned to other tasks.

"Hackett did one of the finest of all malaria control jobs in Italy," commented Paul Russell. "He had to be as skillful in diplomacy as in science, for it was his job to tell the Italians they were doing it all wrong."

Neither drainage nor quinine by itself could redeem the Pontine Marshes, but the addition of Paris green did. So Mussolini succeeded where some of Rome's emperors failed. There was not a single permanent dwelling in the Pontina before 1930. By 1940, more than 50,000 Italians lived there, not only in new farm houses but three newly built towns, all supported by 200,000 acres of new farmland. "Malaria still exists as I write," said Hackett in 1937, "but the final victory is no longer in doubt."

15

The Gambiae Gamble

After a third of a century of experience with mosquitoes, virtually nobody in public health talked about eradicating malaria, as some had in the beginning. Indeed, despite the efforts described, there was evidence in the 1930's that malaria was again on the upswing in rural areas of the United States, Europe, and South America. Malariologists were not all pessimists, but nearly all were realists. They could reduce malaria, but they could not end it. Quinine and the newer synthetic drugs introduced by the Germans, such as atabrine, were not enough. Paris green and periodic diligence were not enough.

Then came Dr. Fred L. Soper, a dark and handsome Kansan with a thin black mustache, glittering eye, and fierce, yet good-humored, determination to command every situation; he seemed equally capable of browbeating man or mosquito. The name of Soper dominates the field story of yellow fever control, still to come, but Soper found his way to the center of malaria interest during the great epidemics in Brazil in 1938-40 and again in Egypt in 1944-45. In these campaigns, Soper, who was

an active member of the I. H. D. field staff from 1920 to
1947, had the help of several loyal, able colleagues, for instance the wide-ranging, hard-working Canadian, Dr.
D. Bruce Wilson (1894-1963), who not only saw that
Soper's orders were carried out but often served as the
velvet glove on the iron fist.

The story is told that Dr. Wilson, hot, weary, and
thirsty from a field trip, once sat down at the Long Bar
in Shepheard's Hotel in Cairo and ordered seven mar-
tinis. The astonished bartender asked whether he wanted
them in the course of the evening or all at once. Wilson
said all at once, and when the seven were lined up before
him, in chilled, stemmed glasses, he tossed off the first
and the second in two gulps and then settled down to sip
the rest.

Soper and Wilson recaptured the old dream of Ross
and Watson of eradicating—totally uprooting—malaria.
Their adversary was chosen for them, *Anopheles gambiae*, the most efficient of all mosquitoes in carrying malaria from man to man.

The natural home of gambiae, a long-legged specimen with yellowish and black-spotted wings, is in tropical Africa, where it has made its full contribution to the
reputation of the Dark Continent as the white man's
grave. Its efficiency as a malaria vector derives from its
strong preferences for human blood and for sunlight. It
will breed in just about any sunlit spot of water around
human habitation—the amount collected by a hoofprint
in the barnyard is enough.

World Health Organization malaria experts now figure that, under favorable climatic conditions, gambiae
mosquitoes can saturate a malaria-free population with
vivax malaria in one month and with falciparum malaria

in less than two months. The female mosquitoes are such efficient biters (usually feeding every other day) that they can maintain malaria at a stable level in a community if each person with malaria infects only one mosquito. The calculation is an interesting one because (1) the parasite cycle in this mosquito requires about twelve days before the plasmodia imbibed from one person can be passed to another, and (2) gambiae's natural death rate is about 10 percent per day, meaning only about 30 out of 100 adult mosquitoes survive for twelve days. This is quite enough.

Gambiae's predilection for human habitation explains its tendency to spread beyond its natural habitat, as a fellow traveler in airplanes, boats, trains, and automobiles. This African invader probably first arrived in Brazil by fast mail boat from Dakar.

An I. H. D. entomologist, Raymond C. Shannon (1894-1945), working in the National Yellow Fever Service operated cooperatively by the Brazilian government and the Rockefeller Foundation under Soper's direction, was the first to discover gambiae in Natal, in the State of Rio Grande do Norte, northeast Brazil.

Gathering mosquito larvae in an overflowed, grassy field between the railroad track and the Potengi River on a Sunday morning in March 1930, Shannon counted 2,000 gambiae larvae, for him easily distinguishable from those of Brazilian anophelines. Since the area of infestation was small, Shannon surmised that the importation was recent. Less than one kilometer away, he observed, was the anchorage of the French destroyers which then carried the mail from Africa.

Malaria was a serious endemic problem elsewhere in northeast Brazil, but at the time no cases had been reported in Natal. Five weeks after Shannon's discovery, however, the disease became epidemic in Alecrim, a suburb of Natal. The epidemic quieted down during the dry season and then flared up a second time in Alecrim in January 1931, putting 10,000 of the 12,000 residents to bed.

When Shannon first found the gambiae larvae, he suggested to Soper that they try to exterminate this small focus of the mosquito, and Soper discussed the proposal with the local and national health departments and also the I.H.D. "home office." He wanted to attempt the eradication project, but was advised that he already had his hands full reorganizing the Yellow Fever Service. It was suggested that he leave gambiae to Brazilian authorities.

Between the first and second epidemics, Soper advised local authorities that they open dikes that had been built along the river to convert the tidal flats into freshwater hayfields; he pointed out that flooding the land with salt water would wash out the gambiae breeding spots. The state governor refused permission, however; the field was a source of hay for the horses of the state police.

During the second epidemic, Soper agreed that the Yellow Fever Service should undertake emergency malaria control at Natal until the revolutionary government could get organized to take over. His Service applied Paris green from March until October, when Brazilian federal and state workers took over; they continued with the larviciding until the following April. Gambiae mosquitoes completely disappeared from Natal (never to return). In 1932, drought, famine, and other diseases preempted official attention.

There was no serious outbreak of malaria in the

northeast for the next five years, although from time to time the Yellow Fever Service identified gambiae larvae or mosquitoes elsewhere in Rio Grande do Norte. In 1935, Soper made a trip to South Africa, and learned from Park Ross that the best way to knock out gambiae-transmitted malaria was to spray houses with pyrethrum.

In the first six months of 1938, the greatest epidemic of malaria ever reported in the Americas took place in the states of Ceara and Rio Grande do Norte, in the Jaguaribe, Apodi, and Assu river valleys and up the coast between Natal and Fortaleza.

Gambiae had quietly bred its way about 250 kilometers along the coast and the same distance inland, and now was seeding the population with malaria. People called it "the new disease." Few had any resistance. Whole families had their chills and fever together, with none able to get up and cook or go for quinine. Children went hungry and unattended. There was "a trail of mourning," as almost everyone wore black in memory of one or more relatives freshly laid in their graves.

Well over 100,000 were stricken and 14,000 to 20,000 died. Rarely had the malaria death rate been so high.

The glaring sunlight, steady wind, shimmering heat, and sparse vegetation of northeast Brazil proved an ideal incubator for gambiae, although now, in the rainy season, the mud made it difficult for the Brazilian and Rockefeller health men to move about.

The epidemic peaked in May and June of 1938. Official action now came quickly enough. President Getulio Vargas of Brazil decreed organization of an Antimalaria Service. This federal agency was given a $50,000 budget.

The money largely went for quinine and atabrine to relieve the suffering sick. No Paris green was made available until 1939.

It was observed that Natal itself was still free of gambiae and malaria seven years after the Paris green campaign there in 1932. This fact suggested the desirability of having the Yellow Fever Service again head up another malaria mosquito eradication campaign.

The health men toured the stricken area and met in Fortaleza in November. They recognized that a state of emergency existed. This mosquito might move on, and with it malaria, until much of South America, Central America, even North America, would be in danger of similar fulminating epidemics.

They agreed that the only kind of organization that could move against the problem would be one free of all bureaucratic red tape. Only Soper's Yellow Fever Service met this specification. They formed a new Malaria Service of the Northeast staffed and supplied by the Yellow Fever Service and financed by Brazil and the Rockefeller Foundation. Soper headed it.

The malaria objective was definite: total eradication of *A. gambiae*. The chance of accomplishing this was quite another matter. As Soper and Wilson later wrote in their book, *Anopheles Gambiae in Brazil, 1930 to 1940* (1943), "No one could predict success in an attempt at species eradication, but those cognizant of the situation . . . could predict certain disaster . . . should an attempt at eradication not be made."

At first, the Malaria Service did not get anywhere. Older malaria control methods proved unsuccessful. Paris green larviciding had been demonstrated as an effective method for a limited area of Natal, but there was no precedent in Brazil for its use for species eradication in a large region. It was a matter of field experimentation. Success came only after Marshall Barber visited the program and in May 1939 demonstrated how Paris green could be broadcast by hand over wide areas. He mixed the chemical with dust, soil, sand, or even pebbles, whatever was immediately available.

They now decided to concentrate on two weapons, Paris green in gambiae breeding places and pyrethrum spray on the ceilings and walls of houses where the mosquitoes rested after each meal of human blood. Every breeding place and every house would have to be treated.

Soper and Wilson planned the entire operation. The affected areas were divided into zones and an inspector made individually responsible for the measures taken in his zone, under a chief inspector who was responsible for a district containing five zones. The chief inspector was in turn responsible to a post, headed by a post physician, who in turn was responsible to a superior physician heading a division.

Looking for mosquitoes against the background of mud walls and thatch roofs is akin to seeking a needle in a haystack, but the workers were trained in the technique. Single-handed combat, using a suction bulb to pluck a mosquito from a wall, gave way to a white, square, concave umbrella held next to the wall while insecticide was sprayed on the ceiling and wall. Any mosquitoes present simply dropped dead on the cloth, for the pyrethrum works fast.

All nonmedical field personnel wore uniforms and carried flags to mark the road and house where they were working. At each house, the inspector left a visit record that his chief could check, while making rounds. This record described what was done and when. The man of the house often would read the entries and comment on irregularities.

Gradually, from January 1939 on, the campaign gathered momentum until, by 1940, it had a working force of 4,000 men.

The work began with the rainy season. Malaria again became epidemic. Sick people pleaded with the health officers to pay attention to them, rather than to the mosquitoes, and could not be wholly denied. The mosquitoes were spreading while the Service was mapping the battle zones and trying to get organized to attack. There were manifold personnel problems, one of which was the fact that Brazil had a law saying a man could not hold a government job without showing a certificate of at least one year's military training, a qualification few country people would meet; eventually a special exception was made.

Even with the system of supervision, it was hard to maintain the discipline that assured each inspector would be energetic and efficient. Barber said that the program was not getting the desired results because the shade-loving Service was failing to contact the sun-loving larvae. Soper was happy to have the criticism.

There were a few successes, "carefully nourished rays of hope," in the first six months—a coastal village, a labor camp, and a stretch of highway now free of gambiae. As larviciding accelerated on a wider front by the end of 1939, however, encouraging results began to mount: Caponga, Forquilha, Bom Successo, Carius, Assu, Lake Piato, São Gonçalo. Local cynics said the mosquito disappeared because of the dry season.

The rainy season was early in 1940. Almost everywhere, however, the mosquito appeared to be giving way before Soper's divisions, whereas in two control districts, left to the last, it was still gaining. Lewis Hackett, now back from Italy, dropped by northeast Brazil for an expert look-see and suggested an acid test. No gambiae had been found in Ico Division, in Salgado Valley, once heavily infested, for three months. Why not stop larviciding and insecticiding there and see what happened? Work was stopped, but nothing happened. The mosquito was gone and did not come back.

By mid-1940, Soper and Wilson, shuffling maps, checking lists, and talking continuously of "clean areas" and "dirty areas," knew what they were doing. They were *eradicating* mosquitoes and malaria. Now it became a contest among workers and divisions to see who could finish first.

Russas Division, the last of the infested areas, had 226 dirty spots in May, 18 in August, and none after September 9, 1940.

On Brazil's Independence Day, September 7, the staff of the Malaria Service of the Northeast, at a luncheon in Fortaleza celebrated the disappearance of gambiae. Outsiders said the celebration was a little premature, but the gambiae gamblers had a sure thing now. In October, a fresh pocket of infestation was turned up in Madalena, just beyond Quixada Division of the territory. It was cleaned out.

The last Brazilian-bred gambiae was collected on November 9, and the last larvae were scooped up on November 14, 1940.

Vigilance was maintained, but no gambiae has been found since then, except an occasional stray mosquito newly imported from Africa. A reward first of $5, and

then of $10, was offered for any employee finding a gam-
biae focus anywhere in Brazil, but no one ever won it.

Some twenty-two months and 260 tons of Paris
green later, epidemic malaria in northeast Brazil had been
conquered. It was not without cost. Some 700 Malaria
Service workers had malaria despite prophylactic treatment. Soper was among them. Some of the larviciders
suffered arsenic poisoning from the Paris green, developing pimples, running sores, and nosebleeds; they all recovered rapidly when removed from this detail. A
child got into a can of Paris green left in a home, ate some,
and died. Deaths of cattle, goats, sheep, and chickens were
blamed on Paris green, unjustifiably. To demonstrate the
safety of the chemical, one inspector put some in his beer
and drank it; he became gravely ill but recovered. Two
persons used Paris green as the instrument of suicide.

The campaign cost $2.1 million, the Foundation's
share being $500,000 and Brazil paying the rest.

In the last analysis, it may be said that victory in
northeast Brazil owed no more to science than it did to
administration—fanatic, driving, perfectionistic leadership. It was not only larviciding and insecticiding but
Soperizing that provided the secret weapon. In this program, following on his successful efforts to eradicate
Aëdes aegypti mosquitoes in the Brazilian coastal cities,
Soper established himself as perhaps the ablest public
health field general since Gorgas. Not everybody liked
the man; it was said of him, rather carelessly and without
validity, that he drove some men to drink and others to
suicide. These were exaggerations. He stuck his neck
out and got results. And he did not proceed blindly. In
advocating the anti-gambiae campaign, he wrote the
I. H. D. New York office in 1938: "There can be no
doubt that we are asking for an enormous headache for

quite some time in offering to organize this program but I see no way to avoid the issue."

As if to prove the Brazilian episode was no fluke, the same methods were successfully applied in the later eradication of gambiae in the Upper Nile Valley in Egypt.

16

Malaria in World War II

Despite the pioneer brilliance of Gorgas and others in the Army Medical Corps' control of insect-borne diseases in the tropics, the United States Army entered the war in the Pacific in 1941 in a state of intellectual desuetude that defies the imagination of all except those who experienced it. The greatest enemy of the troops sent to New Guinea, the Solomon Islands, and other points in the South Pacific was not at first the Japanese with their bayonets and swords but blood-sucking mosquitoes, carrying malaria.

In fact, malaria was the Army's foremost infectious disease problem in the South and Central Pacific, Southwest Pacific, China-Burma-India, and Middle East theaters of war. For the entire Army, in the United States and overseas, 1942-45, malaria ranked second only to gonorrhea (malaria, 377,994 cases; gonorrhea, 881,386).

In many engagements, malaria accounted for more casualties than combat. This was true not only in the South Pacific and Far East but in the Sicilian campaign and at the air bases in West Africa. In the initial stages of the New Guinea campaign, six to eight patients with malaria were evacuated for each battle casualty.

The only Americans trained to cope with malaria overseas were certain members of county, state, and federal public health services and the malariologists, entomologists, and sanitary engineers of the Rockefeller Foundation. They were soon heavily engaged. The experience of Paul F. Russell illustrates the situation.

The International Health Division assigned Russell to the Philippine Islands to investigate malaria in 1929. He remained there five years. His job, he was told, was to find how to control the disease. Russell demonstrated that the culprit was *Anopheles minimus flavirostris* and that it bred in the foothills and not in the coastal plains or the mountains. The fact was of some significance to the United States Army. Early in the century it had built Fort Stotsenburg well up in the hills away from low-lying Manila, not only out of respect for the splendid view but to avoid the "malarious marshes." Unfortunately, minimus was breeding in nearby mountain streams and malaria was a mysteriously frequent visitor in the barracks—"Only by vigorous action . . . was effective control obtained," wrote Russell.

War was coming, as some could see. For example, a good ten years before Pearl Harbor, Russell made a trip to the southernmost island of the Philippines, where the white man had not been seen for some years. The natives mystified him by asking whether the Japanese or the Americans were winning the war. There were signs that Japan was preparing for it. At Davao a Japanese colony was raising hemp. The workers were said to be soldiers of the Emperor's army. Russell discovered that their officers knew the importance of malaria control. The workers, or soldiers, slept in barracks under mosquito nets and every night an old Japanese woman performed her strange job, that of net-tucker-in. The Japanese army, as Russell learned again during the war, suffered greatly from malaria despite efforts to control it.

Russell met General Douglas MacArthur in the Philippines. MacArthur, then Chief of Staff of the United States Army (and later, following his first retirement, Field Marshal of the Philippine Army), also feared the intentions of Japan. He requested Russell's assignment to an Army malaria control survey of the Bataan Peninsula. Already he was planning how to meet a Japanese invasion.

Russell and Major Rufus L. Holt of the Army Medical Corps found Bataan a wild jungle of thorns and snakes, and a potential malaria hotspot. Their luggage bearers were Negritos, small bushmen who carried sixty pounds on their backs. They slept on rocks in streams to avoid the snakes in the bushes. Breeding in these streams were minimus mosquitoes. Russell and Holt wrote malaria control recommendations that became a part of MacArthur's plan but that unfortunately he could not put into use when the time came. The Japanese overpowered the jungle stronghold and precipitated the Death March. The Bataan malaria mosquitoes strafed both victor and vanquished.

Russell was in India when Japan attacked Pearl Harbor. Returning to the United States, he took military leave from the Foundation and, as a lieutenant colonel, in 1942 became chief of the tropical medical section in the Preventive Medicine Service of the Army Surgeon General's Office. In March 1943, MacArthur requested, through General Marshall, that Russell report to him. Russell arrived at MacArthur's headquarters in Brisbane in May.

"Doctor," said the General, "this will be a long war if for every division I have facing the enemy I must count on a second division in the hospital with malaria and a third division convalescing from this debilitating disease."

MacArthur, now in command of the Southwest Pacific Area, said that he had signed every directive on malaria control prepared by his medical officers, but malaria continued to plague his troops. Further, he was not getting any information on where the trouble lay. He asked Russell to investigate in the combat zones and report back.

Russell found line officers generally indifferent to mosquitoes. For example, in New Guinea he talked to a commanding general handicapped at the time with a 40 percent malaria casualty rate in his troops. "If you want to play with mosquitoes in wartime," this general told Russell, "go back to Washington and stop bothering me. I'm busy getting ready to fight the Japs."

Following Russell's report, MacArthur removed the New Guinea general from his command and sent *him* back to the United States.

Upon the basis of Russell's recommendation, MacArthur now established a system that proved effective throughout the Army. He gave first priority to the movement of malaria personnel and supplies and he made prophylaxis against malaria a line, rather than a medical staff, responsibility. MacArthur made it the duty of every unit commander to see that every soldier took his atabrine every day. Quinine was in short supply, the Japanese having cut off the source in Indonesia. It was replaced by atabrine in 1943, after American chemists solved the problem of mass production. The drug did not protect a soldier from infection, but suppressed all symptoms as long as he took it; when he left the combat zone and

stopped taking atabrine, he often became sick. Chloroquine, likewise of German origin, eventually replaced
atabrine after the war. Lowell T. Coggeshall and John
Maier had done the first testing of chloroquine in the
United States as part of the I.H.D. Laboratories' malaria chemotherapy screening program.

General MacArthur also put into effect Russell's
recommendation that malaria control and survey teams,
which General Marshall had authorized, be attached to
each combat force in a malaria zone. The task of such
teams is the same in war as it is in peacetime—to find the
mosquitoes that transmit malaria and fight them at both
ends, breeding and biting. Warfare continuously creates
places where water can collect. Every wheel rut, foxhole,
tank track, shell hole, or machine-gun nest is a possible
jumping-off place for malaria.

Under Russell's chief, Brigadier General James S.
Simmons (1890-1954), head of the Preventive Medicine
Service, mosquito survey and control units were organized and trained as rapidly as possible. The Rockefeller
Foundation provided facilities for training—malaria
schools for officers—at Jacksonville, Pensacola, and Tal-
lahassee, Florida. By the end of the war, the Army had
161 malaria control and 72 survey units overseas, each
made up of 12 or 13 men.

The Army malaria rates overseas reached their
peak in August 1943, and dropped markedly thereafter
despite expanding operations in malarious areas. The drop
coincided with the building up of a malaria control system. When the need was realized, malaria control men
and material were moved from tenth to first priority in
overseas shipment. No longer were they, as Russell had
found, left standing on the dock in San Francisco.

Recapitulating "Lessons in Malariology from World

War II," Russell commented: "Contrary to press statements, it definitely was not DDT which brought down the rates. They subsided more than a year before DDT became available in practical amounts." The decisive factors were a "malaria-conscious command" and abandonment of the idea that "a doc is a doc." Army medical officers were helpless until they were backed up by specialists trained to fight the anopheline-plasmodian axis.

17

DDT: The Bugs Bite the Dust

DDT, one of those products that reduced the American press to happy babble about "magic" and "miracle," had a dull beginning. Othmar Ziedler (182?-1892), a German pharmacist studying chemistry at Strasbourg, synthesized dichlorodiphenyltrichloroethane from chlorine, alcohol, and sulphuric acid in 1874. He made a note of the new chemical compound in the journal of the German Chemical Society and got on with his studies. Thus, science had the answer to malaria prevention in its hands before it knew just what needed preventing and without realizing that this chemical was the most devastating insect poison ever invented. Not until World War II did chemical and mosquito meet, and Rockefeller Foundation malariologists helped to bring them together.

DDT—the British were the first to call it that—was rescued from oblivion by Paul Müller (1899-1965) of the J. R. Geigy Company of Basel, Switzerland, who synthesized it as one of a series of related compounds in a search for new insecticides. The company was more interested in mothproofing, but Müller first tried DDT on flies. DDT, either in spray or dust form, killed them in astounding numbers. Müller in 1948 won the Nobel Prize in medicine for his discovery, singular because of one thing: He observed that DDT, wherever it fell, had a staying power, or "residual action," not found in other insecticides.

DDT completely lacked the quick knockout power of pyrethrum. An insect coming in contact with this new menace showed no effects for about twenty minutes; it then went into a drunken spin and fell to the floor, paralyzed. It might not die for several hours. On the other hand, a dusted or sprayed surface remained lethal to insects landing on it for weeks and months, whereas pyrethrum killed only those present at the time it was sprayed. These facts and their significance gradually emerged in the course of World War II. DDT's first commercial application was against the Colorado potato beetle then plaguing Swiss farms. Its use in Switzerland soon widened, against plant, animal, and human diseases. When French refugees from the Nazi invasion came across the border, the Swiss deloused them with DDT.

British and American military observers learned that the Germans were receiving large shipments of DDT for use against lice on the Russian front, and sent samples to the United States and Great Britain in 1942. One sample came to Paul Russell's desk in the Surgeon General's Office. He sent it to Barber in Florida for testing against anopheline larvae. Other samples went to the Department of Agriculture and its Bureau of Entomology made tests; the results were remarkable. The Cincinnati Chemical Works began mass production of DDT in 1943. So did the British.

Never had a discovery occurred at a better time. The pyrethrum daisy crop in Kenya had failed while the

War Department was trying to increase production of insecticides to meet a vast military demand. Pyrethrum was in short supply and being limited to use among armed forces overseas.

The Bureau of Entomology undertook large-scale experiments on DDT against mosquitoes at its Orlando, Florida, laboratory, under the direction of Fred C. Bishopp, Walter E. Dove (1894-1961), and Edward F. Knipling. The chemical was a dramatic success, both as a larvicide dust and a house spray. Its residual killing effect was fully confirmed in cages and on the walls of houses.

The first mass demonstrations of the effectiveness of DDT in the control of typhus and malaria were carried out in Italy by teams of civilian doctors, some in uniform, who were members of the Rockefeller Foundation Health Commission.

The Commission in essence was the International Health Division reorganized for war, actually a branch of I.H.D. It was largely the idea of Wilbur A. Sawyer (1879-1951), who had succeeded Frederick Russell as director in 1935 and now also became director of the Health Commission, with George K. Strode (1886-1958), associate director, second in command. The rest of the Commission likewise was drawn from the I.H.D. staff. Sawyer saw the question of what to do in wartime this way:

The plagues of armies and civilians during war were mainly four: typhus, influenza, malaria, and yellow fever. The Foundation already had major programs in yellow fever and malaria control and, in its laboratories, had done promising influenza virus research under Dr. Thomas Francis, Frank L. Horsfall, Jr., George K. Hirst, and their associates. Sawyer promptly set out to remedy the lack of a typhus program by going to Harvard and inducing Dr. Hans Zinsser (1878-1940), the leading American authority on typhus, to train an assistant— John C. Snyder—for overseas work with the I.H.D. on typhus vaccines.

Of all the plagues of war, louse-borne typhus fever is the most feared. It is caused by *Rickettsia prowazeki,* a microbe somewhere between a virus and a bacterium. The disease is carried by the human body louse. People or their bedding have to be in close contact, for the louse can crawl but not fly. During peacetime, only ignorant people with low standards of personal cleanliness suffer from typhus; during war, when vast numbers of soldiers and civilians are on the move, when they are cold, heavily clothed, unable to wash and change their underwear, and are thrown together at night, typhus may become epidemic. The disease is a great killer; typhus investigators often dedicate their articles to colleagues who died of it; for example, Howard T. Ricketts (1871-1910), an American, and Stanislas von Prowazek (1875-1915), of Czechosolovakia, discoverers of the cause, both succumbed to typhus. The disease produced enormous mortality in southern and eastern Europe during and after World War I, killing some twenty million Russians.

Prevention of typhus under the conditions of war never has been a simple matter. Five types of vaccine were available when Snyder began working with Zinsser at Harvard in 1939, but those that were not dangerous were ineffective. No specific treatment was available and the method of ridding people of lice was the same as in World War I—by heating people's clothing while they take a bath. This was cumbersome, time-consuming, and expensive where many persons were involved; in any event, they soon became reinfested.

During an outbreak of typhus in Spain in 1940, Snyder experimented with the chick-embryo vaccine developed by Herald R. Cox; despite the vaccine, Snyder got typhus. He recovered in two weeks. A more potent form of the vaccine was administered to millions of American soldiers on a for-what-it-is-worth basis. Some authorities thought it was of no value, but the eventual conclusion was that, while it would not always protect against infection, the vaccine usually saved the life of the patient.

It appeared highly desirable to sharpen the attack on the louse following an epidemic of typhus in Algeria. In 1942, President Roosevelt by executive order created the United States of America Typhus Commission. The Commission, originally composed of representatives of the Army, Navy, Public Health Service, and Rockefeller Foundation, established headquarters in Cairo, Egypt. Snyder, Soper, and Charles M. Wheeler, an entomologist, were members from the I.H.D., but Snyder and Wheeler accepted Army commissions and Soper withdrew to head the Rockefeller Foundation Health Commission typhus team that Sawyer meanwhile had formed. Other team members were William A. Davis, Floyd S. Markham, and Louis A. Riehl.

At home, this team worked with the Bureau of Entomology of the Department of Agriculture in the search for new louse powders. Compounds were screened for potency against lice. The best of these proved to be good old pyrethrum, in a powder called MYL.

Soper, Wheeler, and Snyder undertook a field demonstration of MYL in two Egyptian villages. The people were undressed and the inner surfaces of their clothing dusted with MYL powder. Nurses were assigned to attend the women during this process and furnish them hospital gowns. The burden of lice per person was greatly reduced. In one village of 2,000, where forty-four cases of typhus occurred, spread of the infection ceased eighteen days after 95 percent of the population had been dusted. Soper counted this as a great success; there had been 300 to 400 typhus cases in villages of similar size that had not had dusting. But some members of the U.S.A. Typhus Commission were not impressed, because many lice remained. Also, in March 1943, Soper himself got typhus, despite having had typhus vaccines several times.

The Rockefeller typhus team—Soper, Davis, Markham, and Riehl—gathered in Algiers in July 1943 for a new attack on lice, with the sponsorship of the State Department and the Pasteur Institute of Algiers. Davis had visited Orlando shortly before coming overseas and brought five pounds of DDT with him, the first available for field testing against body lice. The situation was perfect for an experiment. There was no typhus there at the time. Undisturbed by the pressures of an epidemic, the team concentrated on applying MYL and DDT to the louse-infested population of the Maison Carrée prison near Algiers.

The two insecticides appeared equally effective, but DDT had a prolonged action; MYL, only an instantaneous one. Neither chemical affected the nits, or louse eggs, glued to clothing or hairs. Later, when they hatched, however, the residual DDT killed the newly born lice. DDT remained in cloth for several weeks, even after washing. The team sought experience in delousing urban and rural people at L'Arba. Although in Egypt the Mohammedan women had been persuaded to undress for delousing, a French doctor assured Soper that the Mohammedan women in Algeria would never disrobe, even for a medical examination.

In Egypt, the group had experimented with a small dust gun, in powdering heads and clothing that had been removed, but no advantage had been observed. Soper now remembered that John Ferrell had kidded him about the possibility of having to do delousing in harems and had mentioned using a blower and rubber tube. The team got hold of a dust spray gun, pumped by hand, of the kind used in the North African vineyards. Soper tried it on Riehl as he stood there, blowing the dust up his sleeves, down his neck, and under the waistband of his pants. The dust appeared to penetrate everywhere underneath his clothing. The Arabs were pleased with this new approach, men and women alike. One great gain in not removing their clothes was that the time required per individual was cut from fifteen or twenty minutes to a minute or less.

In September, Soper reported the innovation by messenger to the Typhus Commission in Cairo. The following winter the Rockefeller civilians had the opportunity to furnish a dramatic demonstration to the military.

Allied troops took Naples on October 1, 1943, just as that city, bombed out and now badly overcrowded, was being thoroughly seeded with typhus. Soper got wind of the epidemic there a few days before from a British broadcast of a refugee's story. He went to General Julius Holmes, head of the Allied Military Government for Italy. A.M.G. headquarters were at the moment still in Algiers. Soper told Holmes that Naples had typhus, but the Rockefeller typhus team had the answer. His team was ready to go to Naples and organize louse control in the civilian population. Holmes approved the move on advice of his medical staff. The Army, however, had had its fill of civilian agencies operating in war zones in World War I, and was hard to persuade. In the absence of an alarming epidemic, the action was delayed. Meanwhile, at Army request, the typhus team demonstrated the new delousing technique in prisoner-of-war camps in Algeria, Morocco, Tunis, and Sicily.

These demonstrations were highly successful, but all of October and November went by without an Army okay for the Naples move. On December 2, Soper went to Holmes and told him he planned to go to Morocco; there were typhus cases there.

"Hell, no, Soper," said Holmes. "I want you to go to Naples. Look at this!"

He showed Soper a cablegram reporting twenty cases in a hospital there.

Soper and Davis were put in uniform without insignia of rank and a week later found themselves in Naples, among more than a million people. This was a good 25 percent more than the normal population, with refugee families living in air-raid shelters, caves, and underground quarries. The retreating Germans had burned the stockpiles of winter coal, dynamited the water reservoirs, and blown up the electric power plant. There was no heat, no water, no light.

Snyder, now a major in the Army and a member of the Typhus Commission, was there, doing case-finding. Apparently, Italian soldiers repatriated from the Russian front had brought back typhus the previous winter and civilian cases had begun to occur in Naples in the spring and summer. But the epidemic did not emerge until November 1943.

The Rockefeller typhus team (Markham and Riehl arrived in due course) fell to work fighting lice, unperturbed by the fact that, officially, its attachments were somewhat complex. It was responsible for all delousing activities throughout the 1943-1944 Naples epidemic, first under the Allied Military Government, and finally under the A.M.G.'s post-combat division, the Allied Control Commission.

In the nearest Army supply dump, Soper found a half million two-ounce tins of MYL louse powder, and some DDT, but no dust pumps. He was contemplating the sorry prospect of going back to the old method of making people undress for their dusting when, simply out of frustration or stubbornness, he decided to take another look around. While he was doing so, a truck drove up and unloaded 108 small dusting pumps, of the kind they had used in Algeria.

The Rockefeller men with the help of nurses and inspectors from the Naples Health Department began dusting people on December 15. They started with some 700 leaving Naples on the first passenger train to depart after Allied occupation. For the next two weeks, they powdered typhus patients and their contacts, concentrating on all people living in the same building with reported cases.

On December 28, the first two public delousing stations were opened, in a school and a hospital. The team began by collaring teen-age children in the street and dusting them by force, sending them away with a message: "If that feels good, tell your friends." To be rid of one's lice, fleas, and bedbugs and get a good night's sleep is as good as a weekend in heaven. The first dustees returned with friends and families and the stations became popular overnight. Soon, fifty stations were dusting, reached a peak of 73,000 persons a day on January 10, 1944. By then, DDT was in good supply.

The epidemic began slowly with an average of one reported case a day in September and October and then accelerated during November to five to seven new cases a day and reached a peak during the week ending December 26 with an average of thirty-two a day. By January 9, 1944, they were down to about twenty a day and in the first week of February were back to six a day. In April, the first zero days were recorded. In and around Naples, there had been 2,000 cases and 400 deaths in ten months. These were Italians. Americans managed to stay free of lice and infection.

As typhus epidemics go, it was a small affair. There is no way of telling how large it would have been without the mass delousing program, in the beginning with MYL and toward the end with DDT, which finally arrived in quantity. It could have been a great plague if the lice had their way. In all, 3 million persons were dusted.

Soper, Markham, and Riehl, as they later wrote, were convinced that dusting was an important factor in arresting and reversing the case trend, and that this result was accomplished by the first 25,000 to 30,000 delousings, between December 16 and 28. These were performed on reported cases and their neighbors and relatives, wherever they slept. Each typhus patient and his close associates became louse-free islands from which the disease could not spread, presumably.

The chart of the epidemic certainly bore out the observation that the typhus attack reached its peak just about fifteen days after contact, or spot, delousing began. The effect of mass dusting—at stations, air-raid shelters, and block by block—appeared to be secondary.

The initiative of the Rockefeller Foundation Health Commission in concentrating on louse control now paid dividends. As the German army retreated in 1944, hundreds of thousands of refugees swarmed into northern Italy, Switzerland, and France. The Swiss called for a *cordon sanitaire*. The Allied High Command asked the typhus experts for an opinion. Soper and Markham surveyed the Italian border. Everybody in the Army seemed to have got the word. DDT, via a battery of dust pumps operated off an air compressor, was being vigorously applied to all travelers and their lice. With summer coming on, typhus would naturally recede. They recommended that the people be allowed to pass freely wherever they desired, as long as they were well powdered.

In all probability, the DDT dusting technique was the reason typhus fever remained of insignificant military consequence in World War II. When the Allied forces crossed the Siegfried Line, they found typhus everywhere in the slave labor camps, prisoner-of-war camps, and extermination camps—Belsen, Buchenwald, and Dachau. The British counted 3,500 typhus cases among Belsen's 45,000 inmates. As their liberators approached and their guards fled, prisoners escaped into the countryside. Never had there been such a quick scattering of typhus germs. Prisoners from the camps in Germany and Austria fled from these countries—but could not cross the border unless they were dusted with DDT. No spread of typhus resulted. War's greatest plague had been crushed, as surely as the Nazis and Fascists themselves.

18

Sardinian Success Story

But there was still malaria.

Thanks to the mosquito control program led by Missiroli and Hackett, Italy by 1939 had a tenth as much malaria as in the 1920's. As the tide of battle swept north from Rome and crested along the Arno River in the summer of 1944, however, it became apparent that the German army had left the Italian farmers facing their old enemy again in the Campagna and Pontina. War canceled previous gains. The Germans sabotaged the great drainage works, flooding the lowlands with the brackish water that *Anopheles labranchiae* preferred. The civilian malaria control service no longer existed. The mosquito came back and with it disease. The population was doubly vulnerable, having lost its biological resistance to malaria as well as its sanitary defenses against the mosquito.

Fortunately, there now arrived on the scene two of the greatest mosquito fighters since Gorgas—Russell and Soper. Paul Russell, now a colonel, was in command of the Allied Military Government's Malaria Control Section in the Allied Control Commission.

If DDT could stop typhus, why not malaria?

Russell and Soper roomed together in Naples and together worked out a plan to carry out a house-spraying experiment in nearby Bonificia di Castel Volturno, a small town surrounded by a marshy area that had been drained and partly settled before the war. At the time of the Italian armistice in September 1943, the Germans destroyed the pumping stations and flooded the good land.

The Allied High Command was now enthusiastic about Rockefeller Foundation civilians. Two more, Dr. Henry Kumm and Frederick Knipe, were summoned and Soper took charge of the new malaria team designated as a Research Unit of the A.M.G. Malaria Control Section. Riehl was the entomologist.

During the spring and early summer of 1944, Riehl with the help of Italians DDT'd the inside walls of every house, stable, and pig sty in the Castel Volturno area. He then studied the effects on labranchiae mosquitoes and the malaria rate.

A dry residue of DDT persisted long after the kerosene solvent evaporated and it killed all mosquitoes that alighted on the walls even for a few minutes. The deadliness to insects of the treated surface remained almost undiminished throughout the malaria season *after only one spraying.*

The public health effect was simple and direct. It stopped the transmission of malaria. The result stunned the minds of malaria workers who in the past had to locate every anopheline breeding place within a mile or two of a house, and then cover the water surfaces with Paris green at weekly intervals, often resorting to crop-dusting airplanes to cover large marshes.

Castel Volturno was the first controlled experiment in which complete interruption of malaria transmission in an entire community was attempted by residual DDT spraying. Individual houses had been sprayed elsewhere in 1942 and 1943. Several towns in other parts of the world were sprayed with DDT later in 1944. The United States Army began, at about the same time, to spray with DDT in the South Pacific islands.

After Rome fell to the Allies in June 1944, Russell and Soper turned their attention to the Tiber Delta, in the middle of the Pontina, a marsh once more. Kumm and Knipe were assigned to the project, to study DDT spray dosage and effects and to develop improved spraying equipment, but the malaria season was well advanced and spraying was limited to two small areas, Ostia and Isola Sacra.

The 1945 program, however, called for the spraying of all buildings in the Tiber Delta and the coastal plain, including Fiumicino and Maccarese. The Allied Control Commission and the Italian government, now coming back to life, agreed that in areas being sprayed with DDT no other antimalaria measures would be used. In other words, the attack would be solely aimed to exploit the habit that, as Hackett pointed out, almost all domesticated anopheline mosquitoes have in common —resting after meals in the shade around the house or barn. This was the undoing of *Anopheles labranchiae.*

The Tiber Delta results were most convincing. The summer was well advanced before the spraying was finished, but the malaria curve, rising steeply in the spring, broke following the spraying. There were but few mosquitoes and only old malaria cases—relapses from previous infections—during the second half of

1945. The "Roman airs" had not evaporated like this before.

The great Italian malariologist, Alberto Missiroli, who had seen some bad days, summed up the 1945 results in a few words: "Not one new case of malaria was found in the Tiber Delta, and Ostia [a town there] achieved a state of health she has not enjoyed for 2,000 years, that is, since Italy was first invaded by malaria."

Missiroli now boldly set the objective of the Italian government: the eradication of malaria in Italy in five years. This seemed feasible, and was in fact accomplished.

But meanwhile Fred Soper, with characteristic boldness, had been pushing the idea of which he was an early, and eventually the foremost, prophet: species eradication as a practical goal in the control of mosquito-borne disease. In Brazil, he, Wilson, and the Brazilian health workers had accomplished species eradication of *Aëdes aegypti*, the carrier of urban yellow fever, in the larger cities, and, as we saw earlier, had eradicated *Anopheles gambiae* in northeast Brazil.

Now that DDT was available, why not try species eradication in Sardinia? Soper suggested the possibility soon after the Allies captured Rome in mid-1944. Missiroli and Hackett, from their experience years before in controlling malaria in Portotorres, knew the labranchiae mosquito in Sardinia, and it, like the mainland branch of the family, had shown itself to be domestic—a target that house spraying could hardly miss.

Sardinia was a tough malaria target, a rough, primitive island abounding in mountains and wide marshy plains, illiterate peasants, shepherds, sheep, goats, bandits, rock lookout towers, and poverty. Sardinia is slightly smaller than New Hampshire but wilder; its

1,250,000 Sards were largely concentrated in isolated inland villages, originally settled to avoid the centuries of slave traders and pirates who landed on Sardinia's shores. What it made up in scenery and Old World picturesqueness of costume and custom, it lost in the lack of good roads, good fortune, and good health.

It took about a year to get the idea across. S. M. Keeny was about to head a mission to Italy from the United Nations Relief and Rehabilitation Administration (UNRRA). Forty-three nations, well aware of the plight of Europe following World War I, had established UNRRA in November 1943 to help the liberated peoples with food, clothing, and shelter, restoration of agriculture and industrial production, and recovery of public health. The UNRRA resources for this one program, health care, totaled about $175 million, or nearly twice what the International Health Division had spent in thirty years. Dr. Wilbur A. Sawyer reached the retirement age of sixty-five as I.H.D. director in 1944, and became UNRRA director of health.

Then in the summer of 1945 DDT knocked labranchiae malaria cold in the Tiber Delta. Enthusiasm for the Sardinia project grew, not only because of the hope of eradicating malaria, which Missiroli embraced for all Italy, but because it offered a contest between exogenous man (Soper) and indigenous mosquito (labranchiae). As the war ended, malariologists were at the point of taunting Soper, in their nice scientific way, that perhaps it had been possible to eradicate gambiae in Brazil and again in Egypt because it was "an introduced, rather than indigenous, species"—a hypothetically unstable vagrant rather than a well-adjusted native. Perhaps it would be a different story with this member of the old maculipennis family, which had been around to bite both ancient Romans and modern, plus all those who dug their graves. Soper regarded the distinction as meaningless.

But what a triumph this would be if the No. 1 Mediterranean malaria mosquito could be eradicated! The historians might overlook it but it would top anything Julius Caesar or Mussolini and their legions had ever accomplished.

The proposal, as it was elaborated, certainly was persuasive. As long as there was the mosquito, malaria might come back. In the long run, mosquito eradication —if at all possible—would be cheaper than the perennial control measures that were effective in response to a present danger and then neglected as the result of success. It should be possible to knock out labranchiae in a year's time and at a cost of less than $3 million. DDT house spray alone ought to do the job if timed to greet the mosquito as it came out of winter quarters, but if it didn't, the project could then fall back on larviciding during the breeding season.

What clinched the proposition was framing it as an experiment in eradication. In October 1945, first the Foundation and then UNRRA and the Italian government officially agreed to undertake an all-out attempt to eradicate *Anopheles labranchiae* from the island for the specified scientific purpose of seeing if eradication of an indigenous species was possible in the Mediterranean area.

In those terms, it was impossible to fail if the experiment was carried to its conclusion, but in retrospect I.H.D. veterans smile and call the Sardinian project a failure. It was a failure only if one recognized what was

in the hearts and heads of men like Soper and Sawyer—
they were convinced that the mosquito could be eradicated or they would not have endorsed the task.

From the start, however, there were signs that the
Sardinian stars were not in scientific conjunction. An
organization was created to carry out the project, *Ente
Regionale per la Lotta Anti-Anofelica in Sardegna*
(ERLAAS), or Regional Agency for the Anti-
Anopheles Campaign in Sardinia. The agency existed
for four and a half years and, at its peak, employed 33,500
trained and untrained workers, but from the beginning
ran into administrative and logistic difficulties and delays.

Soper asked his old team-mate, Bruce Wilson, to
head the project and anticipated working with him. Wilson left the gambiae project in Egypt late in 1945 and
came to Italy, expecting to start work but UNRRA was
unable to deliver supplies and equipment. In early 1946,
Soper left Italy to undertake other I.H.D. assignments.
Paul Russell had returned to the United States in 1944,
so he, too, was out of the picture.

Wilson got the ERLAAS operations under way in
May 1946. The following September, he persuaded another veteran, Dr. J. Austin Kerr, to succeed him as
superintendent. Kerr asked for reassignment in September 1947, and was succeeded by John A. Logan, a civil
engineer, who saw the project through its last three
years. In handy hindsight, it would appear to have been a
mistake not to make Soper, who had the big idea, ag-
gressiveness, and a record for dramatic success, responsible for the Sardinian project. Instead, he was assigned
to Cairo and at the end of 1946 returned to the United
States, where, a few months later, he was elected director of the Pan American Sanitary Bureau, in Washington.
Russell, at the Army Medical School on the other side

of town, was convalescing from an illness and finishing the first edition of his textbook, *Practical Malariology*.

The variety of obstacles encountered in Sardinia is incredible, but the biggest setback occurred right at the beginning and slipped a stiletto into the ideological heart of the theory of mosquito eradication. A mosquito survey made by Dr. Thomas H. G. Aitken, the I.H.D. entomologist, as soon as work began, showed that labranchiae, Sardinian style, was not exclusively the brackish-water breeder and hanger-on around the house that Missiroli and Hackett described.

At the first meeting of ERLAAS, Kerr had said that if they found labranchiae maintaining itself independently of man or living at altitudes of more than 500 meters, "its eradication is not feasible, or even possible." This was precisely what Aitken found. Labranchiae larvae existed in almost every kind of water collection from rock pools by the sea up to mountain peaks of 1,000 meters or more. The mosquito bred in every kind of surface water, brackish or fresh, standing or running. It rested and hibernated in every kind of natural or manmade shelter, both within villages and far away from them. It fed on pigs, horses, and oxen as well as people on the farms, and back in the hills apparently preyed on sheep, goats, birds, and other animals as well as sipping plant juices. In sum, it was no more a house mosquito than an outdoor mosquito.

In view of this finding, it is pointless to detail the three annual house spray campaigns, the trial larviciding in 1947, and the island-wide larviciding in 1948. In 1950, when Logan had achieved the best of a bad situation and UNRRA and the Rockefeller Foundation had had their final annual renewal of financial faith in the project, *Anopheles labranchiae* could still be found on the island.

True, it took 330 man-days of work to find one mosquito, but in total eradication one egg-laying female is one too many. And this rugged mountain mosquito survived in greater number than that.

The Rockefeller Foundation health men, who over the years had learned the public health wisdom of economy, never have ceased to be shocked at how much the Sardinian project cost: nearly $13,000,000, including $778,000 in UNRRA supplies, $11,600,000 from the Italian Lire Fund, and $576,000 from the Rockefeller Foundation.

The per capita cost of the experiment was about four times that of eliminating malaria from the rest of Italy, where no attempt was made to exterminate all mosquitoes.

Yet there was a pleasant by-product of "failure," as there often is in scientific experiment:

Malaria disappeared from Sardinia and did not return.

The International Health Division doctors, all of them, were pretty sure this would happen after the first year. Malaria cases in Sardinia dropped from 75,000 in 1946 to 39,000 in 1947, 15,000 in 1948, and 44 in 1950. In 1950, all the doctors, nurses, schoolteachers, and scouts could turn up only four new cases, the remainder being relapses in old cases. In 1951, there was one new case. From 1951 to 1963, only ten new cases occurred.

Much the same thing happened in the rest of Italy, too. Missiroli's campaign, starting from a base of a half million cases in 1945, brought the total down to a few hundred cases, mainly relapses, in 1951. In 1953, there was only one new case in the entire country.

There were other beneficial by-products in Sardinia. Some 100,000 acres of marshland were cleared, drained, and made available for farming. Thousands of laborers were given employment during a depressed period. And, most of all, Sardinia, a backward country, has been rehabilitated after a long, long illness. It now has a developing agriculture, a growing economy, good roads, wealthy villas, swank resort hotels, and a thriving tourist business. Mosquitoes are few. Malaria has vanished.

The visitor to this island today sees a Sardinian success story, perhaps proving that sometimes it is possible to succeed while failing. Science and money aside, if the purpose of health workers is to improve people's health, then Sardinia was a success story.

19

Malaria Eradication Today

If well begun is half done, as the saying goes, then it might be reckoned that half done is almost finished. Yet it is doubtful that any competent authority could be found who would say that malaria is almost finished, even though it can be shown today that it has been apparently driven out of over half the world where it previously existed, and that its disappearance constitutes in some places one source of a public health backlash—that is, population overgrowth.

In the United States, where the focus of health attention is on heart disease, cancer, and apoplexy, what has happened to world malaria does not excite much interest, even though it involves "the greatest health effort of all times," to quote Soper. In its meaning to people and their health, however, the worldwide reduction in malaria dwarfs victories over such communicable diseases as poliomyelitis, smallpox, cholera, typhus, and yellow fever. On the basis of rough estimates, malaria now strikes fewer than 100 million or so per year as compared to 300 million twenty years ago. These estimates are *very* rough.

The saving in lives and health has been so stupendous that, for the first time in 1966, Dr. Marcolino G. Candau of Brazil, director general of the World Health Organization, was willing to stick his neck out. Previously, Candau had refused to estimate either morbidity or mortality rates for world malaria, being familiar with the lack of reporting from some places and the twin problems in others of failing to report cases or of calling any fever malaria. Now, however, he exulted:

". . . 3,500,000 deaths due to the direct effects of malaria recorded per year in the early fifties are now down to less than one-third of that figure. The number of deaths resulting from malaria today is less than one million per year. I do not have to insist on the humanitarian significance of this trend, but we might usefully stop to consider the economic significance of this change in the mortality figures. If we relate them to morbidity, we may conclude that a reduction of over 200 million cases per year has taken place—200 million people who no longer suffer from malaria nor from the consequent temporary incapacity that results in economic loss to the wage-earner individually and to his country collectively."

WHO's staff of malaria experts measures the progress of malaria eradication efforts in cooperating countries in this way: Of an estimated 1,576 million persons living in the originally malarious areas of the world, 1,304 million, or 78 percent, now live in areas where malaria has been or is being eradicated. India once produced 100 million malaria cases a year, but 90 percent of its population is now free of the disease. Malaria still continues to be the leading health problem in Africa south of the Sahara, where more than half the children under three and almost all the population over that age suffer from the disease.

Following the Castel Volturno and Tiber Delta demonstrations, Dr. Arnoldo Gabaldon of Venezuela was the first to attempt country-wide malaria eradication, beginning in 1945. The national health departments of Italy, in 1946, and the United States, British Guiana, and Ceylon, in 1947, then followed. The progression continued until, by 1965, twenty-seven nations claimed to be controlling malaria and another thirty-eight were listed as countries where malaria never existed or has disappeared without specific measures against it.

Following the termination of the International Health Division in 1951, the Rockefeller Foundation brought its malaria program to a close in a phase-out period that continued until 1954. In a period of thirty-nine years (1915-1954), the Foundation spent $4.9 million against malaria, exclusive of staff salaries and expenses. Compared to the huge sums spent by governments during and since that time, such a small expenditure invites the question of what the International Health Division really accomplished.

The explicit and limited function of a broad-purpose foundation is to attract public attention to a human problem in need of solution, help get demonstrations started, set a good example if possible, induce other agencies to follow it, and then move on. The smallness of the total sum spent as contrasted with its real impact in the advancement of knowledge of malaria prevention tends to confirm the contention of Raymond B. Fosdick that "In the end it is not money that counts; it is *men*." The field of malaria provides impressive documentation. It was, as we have seen, the Roses, Darlings,

Hacketts, Russells, Sopers, Wilsons, and all the others who, together with their British, Italian, Indian, Brazilian, and other national counterparts, had the imagination, courage, and drive to write the antimalaria chapters in the copybook of world health. These men, supported by small sums of risk capital, laid the groundwork in what they learned of the parasite, the insect, and the disease, and in provision of the administrative know-how for the malaria eradication program that developed following World War II.

When the nations of the world formed the World Health Organization in 1948 with an operating program against malaria, the Foundation's pioneering mission was fulfilled. The first World Health Assembly placed malaria at the head of the list of health problems to which it gave priority.

WHO policy followed the pattern of effort established by the I.H.D.—to rely on residual insecticides, to offer technical advice and some financial aid to governments inviting it, to organize demonstration teams made up of outside experts and their national counterparts, to seek prevention of malaria in the areas selected for demonstration. With at first but limited funds and personnel, WHO made a modest beginning in a few countries. Meanwhile, other countries went ahead on their own. By 1950, nearly all the malarious nations of North and South America were engaged in eradication, and about 50 percent of the houses in malarious zones had been sprayed.

WHO defined malaria eradication as meaning a program that in a limited time ends the transmission and eliminates the reservoir of malaria in a given population. Falciparum and vivax malaria die out in infected individuals within three years. Thus an eradication campaign must break the cycle of transmission for at least that time.

The Sardinia experiment dampened any general hope that mosquitoes capable of transmitting malaria in their native haunt could be totally exterminated. At the same time, the impact of DDT was so dramatic that malaria teams everywhere embraced the objective of eradicating the malaria parasite. The last mosquito in the swamp or in the high mountain might elude them but not, they hoped, the last plasmodium seeking passage from one human blood stream to the next. To eradicate the parasite but not the mosquito in a given region, of course, requires continued vigilance against reinfection.

In 1951, a small dark cloud appeared on the horizon. It already had been observed in Italy that houseflies were adapting themselves to DDT; some could crawl on it and buzz off happily. Now came a report from Greece that *Anopheles sacharovi* was developing a resistance to DDT. Some of this species could rest on a sprayed surface without ill effect. As time went on the same phenomenon was observed here and there in Latin America.

Human nature also reared its fickle head. The householder's enthusiasm for DDT came not so much from its capacity to kill mosquitoes and prevent malaria but, in some places, its extermination of flies and, in others, bedbugs, too. When both flies and bedbugs developed a resistance to DDT and continued to disturb them, people turned against the insecticide, malaria or no. This *human* resistance was fed by the great amount of publicity on the rapid reduction of malaria. People assumed malaria was no longer a hazard.

Alarmed malariologists now saw the problem as a

race between eradication and resistance. Repeated DDT-spray campaigns conducted piecemeal over periods of several years would only serve to select out for survival strains of mosquitoes too tough to be poisoned. It was necessary to knock out malaria before their insect resistance or human indifference could develop. Such an approach could be expedited by using additional anti-mosquito measures in areas of resistance. This did not always mean going back to the older methods, such as Paris-green larviciding, although this method is sometimes still used. Now there was quite a list of new residual insecticides, falling either in the chlorinated hydrocarbon class, like DDT, or a group of organic phosphorous poisons.

Fearing a rise in insect resistance, the Pan American Sanitary Conference in 1954 called for immediate activity in a program of continental malaria eradication in the Western Hemisphere. The government of Mexico quickly responded and appealed to the United Nations International Children's Emergency Fund (UNICEF) for help. UNICEF turned to WHO for advice. The World Health Assembly in 1955 considered the Pan American call to arms and topped it by requesting WHO to take the initiative in a program of world-wide malaria eradication. UNICEF came up with the immediate financial aid needed. The International Development Advisory Board of the United States estimated that a five-year program throughout the malarious world would cost about a half billion dollars in international and matching government funds. Congress accepted the challenge by stating in the Mutual Security Act of 1957: "The Congress of the United States, recognizing that . . . malaria . . . constitutes a major deterrent to the efforts of many peoples to develop their economic resources . . . declares it to be the policy of the United States to assist other peoples in their efforts to eradicate malaria." This declaration was backed up by appropriations to various agencies, including the Agency for International Development, the Pan American Health Organization, WHO, and UNICEF.

Under the administration of Candau, who became director general in 1953, WHO has been aggressive in its worldwide malaria eradication efforts. The resistance of the mosquito to insecticides, and also occasionally of the plasmodium to chloroquine or other antimalaria drugs, is not its worst problem. Actually, the great alarm over insect resistance may have distorted the picture. Problems of this sort have arisen, in limited areas of Central and South America and southern Iran, but these have involved only about one percent of areas where eradication programs were in progress. One percent failure is far less than can be expected with most of the so-called wonder drugs.

One great obstacle is what Candau delicately describes as "political instability," especially in some parts of Asia. By this, of course, he means the power struggle —the disruption of government services by such means as armed revolt, civil war, and international warfare. Political and military conflicts not only obstruct peaceful operations but drain away money and personnel. In some places, lack of sufficient money is the primary obstacle to progress.

The greatest remaining reservoir of endemic malaria is in tropical Africa, where malaria prevention, economic development, and political stability are linked problems. Here, malaria is the chief communicable disease, and accounts for about two thirds of the world's cases. Malaria prevention has only begun in tropical Africa.

Malaria, although one of the greatest miseries of human history, is not a dramatic disease like yellow fever. Yet, paradoxically, it has had a way of making itself conspicuous in its absence. The measure of its previous impact in some of the developing countries is the way mothers and children blossom and the population booms. Such an effect is rarely seen in other categorical, or specific, disease-prevention campaigns.

There are biostatistical difficulties in establishing cause-and-effect relationships between public health efforts and general decline in mortality. Generally speaking, an effective attack on a single disease, such as typhoid fever, does not become clearly and directly visible as a reduction of the total annual death rate of a large population. The result is quite different, however, with insecticide-implemented malaria eradication programs in countries where the disease is a so-called hyperendemic problem affecting great masses of poor and illiterate people who do not even know the words "sanitation" or "hygiene." In the space of only a few years, the total death rates of these countries plunged downward, sometimes as much as 50 percent and, conversely, their populations began an upward spiral.

The malariologists, after years of struggle to lift the human burden of chills and fever, were reminded of the point made by Walt Whitman: "It is provided in the very essence of things that from any fruition of success, no matter what, shall come forth something to make a greater struggle necessary."

The success born of DDT took the experts by surprise. Perhaps they should not have been surprised, but they were. You will remember that Wickliffe Rose, visiting Malcolm Watson in Malaya in 1914, learned that on one plantation fifty Tamil women had been unable to bear a living child prior to malaria control, but Watson changed this by killing malaria mosquitoes through drainage. It became clinically well known that malaria and the anemia accompanying it are a serious complication in pregnancy, often acting as aborters and killers of mother and newborn child. In other words, the disease provides a pathological form of birth control in heavily malarious regions. It was also known, of course, that malaria was a complicating factor in various other diseases, both organic and infectious. Its total effects on maternal, infant, and general mortality had not been measured, however.

What impressed the malariologists was that, by depressing population and the vitality of the people, the disease depressed agricultural growth and development, often preventing colonization of lands that looked, from outside mosquito range, like paradise. Their professional bias was saving lives, so when discussion turned to population growth in the absence of malaria they tended to regard this as a normal and favorable outcome, and to dismiss views of "portentous alarm by those who lack faith in the operation of normal biological balances in the case of the human race," as one said.

But DDT was unlike anything anyone had ever known. It is at least a quadruple threat, killing not only the mosquitoes that carry malaria but the fleas that carry bubonic plague, the lice that carry typhus, and the flies that carry typhoid, dysentery, and probably other diseases. As a matter of fact, DDT and other insecticides bear about the same threatening relation to the insect as the nuclear bomb to humanity. Insecticides are the one measure of disease prevention that has been immediately related to the population explosion.

The singular characteristic of DDT is that it can be applied with maximum effectiveness without any change in the educational, cultural, or economic status of the persons benefited. This is a mixed blessing. Sanitary sewerage and a safe municipal water supply work in the same depersonalized manner, irrespective of individual effort or interest, but have a great drawback compared to DDT house spray in that imponderable difficulties sometimes arise in persuading the would-be beneficiaries to use toilets and faucets. We saw in the hookworm campaign how difficult it is to persuade unenlightened people to use privies rather than the outdoors. Among people who do not understand about bacteria, it is sometimes difficult to break the habit of using a polluted water supply in preference to a safe one. All DDT requires, on the other hand, is for a spray team to move through the houses of a village a couple of times a year; the residual effect on bugs landing on the ceiling and walls does the rest. The people need only say, "Come in."

Ceylon and British Guiana, both early scenes in the campaigns against hookworm and malaria and in the development of rural health services, have become much-cited examples of population explosion following malaria eradication.

In Ceylon, for example, the crude death rate in 1940 was still 20.1 per 1,000, or about twice that of advanced countries. Twenty years later, in 1960, the rate was down to 9.1, or less than that of the United States.

Irene B. Taeuber, of the Office of Population Research, exploring the question of why governments and international planners were caught napping on the population problem, explained what happened:

"In late 1946 and early 1947 the public health services of Ceylon had the houses of the island sprayed with DDT. The death rate was cut 40 percent in a single year. In the short run, the ties that bound death rates to levels of living and ways of living were snapped."

At a reported cost of two dollars per capita, the people of Ceylon acquired a modern life expectancy. A great deal of land previously in the possession of malaria mosquitoes was opened up for cultivation. But there was this ironic catch: more living babies.

In 1965, Peter Newman, a public health economist from the University of Michigan, was able to specify the increment—substantially but not entirely due to malaria eradication. Without DDT, one million of the Ceylon population of ten million alive by 1960 would not have been born. "Malaria eradication is estimated to have contributed about 60 percent of the postwar acceleration of population in growth in Ceylon, and about 40 percent in British Guiana. . . ." Newman pointed out that the veteran health officer of British Guiana, Dr. George Giglioli, was able to arrive at some estimate of the extent that "the great debilitator" malaria reduced general healthiness and resistance to disease. His investigation showed that both in British Guiana and Ceylon four to five times the number of deaths reported as caused by malaria were in some way actually related to malaria. For example, malaria figures heavily in the high death rate from the kidney disease, nephritis.

Failing to predict the spectacular effects of DDT, further reinforced by the therapeutic punch of the antibiotics against bacterial diseases, many countries found themselves with modern death rates but ancient birth rates. This "demographic gap" took the demographers by surprise, too. They were accustomed to see birth rates gradually decline as civilization advanced. Now they had difficulty keeping up with population growth in their predictions.

The results have deeply disturbed public health doctors, who measure the value of their work by the number of human lives saved—all lives, not just of "our people" but of "other people." They have been criticized for shortsightedness and a lack of balance in their objectives, for early failures to relate their efforts to agricultural and industrial development, to national and family planning. Recriminations are pointless. It is enough here to emphasize that prevention of malaria is an absolutely necessary first step in the development of modern civilization. Prevention of people—the starving, ignorant, and impoverished people unable to lift themselves up— is another problem. Universally, mothers and fathers want children who will grow up and survive them; in traditional cultures, where infectious diseases, combined with poor nutrition, injuries, and other factors, may take half the children before the age of ten, parents first need to be shown that they no longer have to produce large families to be sure of some survivors. Thus, to reduce the birth rate first requires a reduction of the death rate in children.

So medical science must go on preventing disease, and our particular hero, the public health doctor, remains a hero, albeit an altogether human one.

COSTLY VICTORY—
YELLOW FEVER

20

Great Men, Great Deeds, Great Mistakes

While yellow fever provides a great success story in preventive medicine, the romanticist might say that this disease seemed to have been put on earth to teach learned men humility. The lesson was not always grasped by the participants in each step of the progress of knowledge against a pestilence that, for drama, has everything. Happily, civilization's terror of this disease of sudden fever, disintegrating liver, yellowing skin, and black vomit is largely a thing of the past, although the virus can still be found lurking in the tropical rain forests of South and Central America and Africa.

In our contemplation of yellow fever as a teaching device, Dr. Benjamin Rush (1745-1813)—colonial America's leading physician at the end of the eighteenth century, a signer of the Declaration of Independence— becomes the first of several cases in point. Wilson G. Smillie called Rush "a fool of the highest order," explaining, "it becomes quite clear that he did more to retard medical progress in the United States than any other one man."

Smillie based his statement on the yellow-fever epi-

demic that struck Philadelphia in 1793. Four thousand
—one of every ten Philadelphians—died of the disease
between August 1 and November 9. Yellow fever already was well known as a hazard of world travel. For
reasons no one then could explain, it was notoriously a
disease of seaports and sailing ships. It would sweep
through a city and then after a few months fade out, not
to return until perhaps years later.

There were 135 major yellow-fever epidemics in
American port cities between 1668 and 1893. Indeed,
hardly a port in the Western Hemisphere escaped the
fury of "yellow jack" (named for the quarantine flag)
in the long period of maritime adventure and trade following the discovery of America.

Once people knew yellow fever's devastation, they
lived in dread of its return. In the face of an epidemic,
thousands of American Southerners might flee north
by train. The city of Jackson, Mississippi, established a
shotgun roadblock against people from towns where
yellow fever was reported. Negroes crossing the fields
were shot. The disease not only destroyed lives, but
indirectly property, too. Sometimes, city authorities ordered the burning of clothing, household goods, and
even the homes of families who had been stricken. The
burning of sulphur, both in the streets and in houses, was
also thought to ward off infection.

Actually, yellow fever is not the all-devouring mon-
ster that human behavior made it appear. As in most infections, its symptoms range all the way from the mild-
est, flu-like indisposition to horrible death. The classic
clinical picture is built around severe cases. The illness strikes suddenly, three to six days after the bite
of an infected mosquito. There is headache, backache,
chills, nausea, and fever of 103° or 104°. The patient is

intensely restless, his tongue a bright red, lips swollen, face flushed, eyes inflamed.

In this first stage, lasting three or four days, the virus circulates in the blood, and it is only at this time that the patient can infect a mosquito that bites him. The second stage is one of deceptive improvement; the fever may ease and the patient feels better. The third stage is one of bodily intoxication. The fever returns. The complexion changes to a dusky, sometimes yellow-ish pallor. There is sometimes *el vomito negro*, a black vomitus that is blood altered by stomach acids. The blood comes from the stomach wall. Bleeding may also occur in tiny spots in the gums of the mouth and in the skin anywhere.

Faget's sign—named for Jean Charles Faget (1818-1884), the French doctor who discovered it—appears early. It is a slowing pulse rate during a high or rising fever, just the opposite of what you would expect. The patient may lose blood proteins in his urine; jaundice from a disturbed bile and liver function may yellow his skin, but the color is seldom as marked as the name "yel-low fever" suggests. Most deaths occur on the sixth or seventh day. If the patient survives the assault on his liver and kidneys, he will recover completely and walk away with a solid immunity against another attack. Counting every infection and not just severe cases, one authority puts the expected death rate at 5 to 10 percent. The most effective treatment for yellow fever is abso-lute quiet in bed.

Rush was the first doctor in Philadelphia to diagnose yellow fever and inform the city fathers of its presence in 1793. He himself got it but recovered. His sister and three of his five young apprentices died of it. Rush re-turned to his rounds, moving continuously from the bedside of one patient to the next, hundreds of them. He got little sleep or time to eat. People pounded at his door in the night for him to come at once; during the day, they crowded into his living room and followed him into the dining room. The doctor could not get away from the smell of sulphur, from his breaking-point fatigue, his tossing insomnia at night, and the nagging question, "Why?"

If he obtained no rest, his burning, vomiting patients fared little better under his treatment. He purged them with jalap and calomel, fed them tincture of cinchona bark, bled and blistered them. He ordered them doused with buckets of cold water. Three or four patients died following this chilling shock, and he reduced the prescription for others to a cold-water enema and a cold cloth on the head.

But he persisted in his blood-letting. The higher the fever, the more blood he took—sometimes as much as three quarts. He called this "a cure." Since yellow fever itself causes patients to lose good blood, through the breakdown of liver function and multiple tiny hemorrhages, Rush's patients undoubtedly succumbed as much to the doctor's treatment as to the disease.

Rush's great stamina brought him through this and three more yellow-fever epidemics, and he lived to write an authoritative text, *Medical Inquiries and Observations*. Rush insisted that yellow fever was not, as everybody thought, contagious. It did not, he said, spread by contact of one person with another. Therefore there was no cause for people to panic, to turn against friends and desert their own husbands, wives, or children. He was right about this.

Obviously the disease got around somehow, however. Rush thought he could explain it. According to his theory, yellow fever was simply a variety of one basic fever arising from a disease of the blood system. This blood disease itself was due, he maintained, to a general debility caused by one of several factors, such as miasma or violent emotion.

Rush attributed the 1793 epidemic in Philadelphia to the odor from a pile of spoiled coffee that had been thrown on Mr. Ball's wharf on the Delaware River. A similar noxious effluvium, he later wrote, could be produced by almost any decaying thing—cabbages, for example. Rotting vegetables were definitely worse than animal matter, he said.

He did not recognize, as some people deduced even then, that the yellow fever was brought in from the West Indies. A sailing ship had tied up at Mr. Ball's wharf. Rush did note that the weather had been hot and dry that summer; there was much stagnant water in streams, springs, rain barrels, and cisterns: "Moschetoes, the usual attendants of a sickly autumn, were uncommonly numerous." But he attached no possible significance to mosquitoes.

The epidemic ended with the first frost. The mosquitoes disappeared, but Dr. Rush explained that people had closed their windows to keep out the chill and so kept out the miasma. Malaria and yellow fever stopped with freezing weather, whereas measles and smallpox continued. The difference was simple, he said: Yellow fever came in through open windows; these other fevers spread from person to person indoors because closing the windows kept fresh air out! The doctor had you either way! Such curious views, comprising the filth, or miasma, theory of disease, dominated medical thinking through the nineteenth century and overlapped the advent of bacteriology and epidemiology.

We have examined the plight of Rush not from any special delight in the quaint or antiquarian but because his story, blending courage, conviction, and folly, sets the stage for what is to come. He epitomized the state of ignorance that had to be overpowered, state by state as it were, to achieve prevention of yellow fever. Similar pitfalls and setbacks awaited others.

21

Mosquito Hunters

"When I was a boy," wrote Lewis Hackett, "everybody thought yellow fever was carried by travelers in their clothes and baggage, else why should it break out in ships on the high seas?" The answer to his question, long in emerging, was a small, silvery mosquito originally from tropical Africa. It is known as *Aëdes aegypti,* freely translated as "unpleasant Egyptian." The female of the species is fond of human blood. Paradoxically, the yellow-fever virus became a rare visitor in temperate-zone seaports long before this mosquito was incriminated as its carrier.

Two technological developments tended to push yellow fever back into its tropical home. One was the modern steamship. The other was a piped city water supply. The aegypti mosquito in the Western Hemisphere insists on reproducing as close as possible to its lunch counter, man. It lives in his house and lays its eggs in his water containers—any cistern, barrel, jug, pot, vase, gutter, old tire, or tin can will do, so long as it contains water that is clean and not salty. The holy water fonts of the village churches in Latin America were

favored aegypti incubators. In West Africa, the natives
kept clay "juju" pots by the doors of their huts to ward
off the jujus, or evil spirits; these pots contained all manner of things: knives, floating eggs, bits of wood, and
many aegypti larvae.

The open water casks on sailing ships were ideal
breeding spots, whereas the closed water systems on
steamships offered little opportunity for egg-laying.
Storing water about the house becomes unnecessary
when there are faucets. Thus, civilization and its inven-
tions helped the public health man fight disease even before he got his science straightened out.

Dr. Josiah C. Nott (1804-1873) of Mobile, Alabama, was one of the first to think of mosquitoes as carriers of yellow fever. Nott also had another distinction;
in 1854, he delivered "Willie" Gorgas, who would show
the world that his mother's physician was right. Six years
before, in 1848, Nott published an elaborate report that
brought him some ridicule. In it, he voiced the suspicion
that yellow fever and malaria, then not specifically dif-
ferentiated from one another, were conveyed by the bite
of an insect, quite likely mosquitoes.

Until overwhelmed in the late 1800's by the experimental evidence that germs are the source of infectious
disease, the medical profession thought otherwise. It
stuck to the Rush concept that filth produced gases
affecting the "humors," or body fluids, and these produced the fever. The smell of sewer gas was sufficiently
offensive to be convincing.

Dr. David Hosack (1769-1835) of New York had
come very close to putting his finger on the pivotal clue
to the mosquito link as early as 1814, the year after Rush's
death. Hosack observed that in every epidemic visitation
of the yellow fever, several days, such as from eight to

twelve to fourteen, have generally elapsed between the first cases that appeared and the communication of it to other persons even in the same neighborhood.

Why was this?

The significance of the question was lost from view for another eighty-three years, and even Dr. Carlos J. Finlay (1833-1915) of Cuba overlooked the point in his spirited insistence on the mosquito theory. Finlay was a physician of Scotch-French descent who lived in Havana. Outside of his practice, he had two grand passions, the liberation of Cuba (1) from Spain and (2) from yellow fever. In 1881, he reported that yellow fever was transmitted from man to man by a mosquito, *Culex fasciatus,* later named *Stegomyia* (meaning "roof fly"). The modern name is *Aëdes (Stegomyia) aegypti.* He was struck by the fact that yellow fever and the mosquito were always found together, and he claimed experimental transmission by mosquito bites in five cases. Finlay's medical colleagues put him down as a harmless crank and, when he persisted, demanded incontrovertible evidence. He fell to raising mosquitoes and used them in more than a hundred experiments, allowing the mosquitoes to bite yellow-fever patients and then healthy persons. A few got yellow fever, but he could not prove to other doctors that these people had acquired the disease from his mosquitoes. Only his wife and his assistant believed him.

Just before the turn of the century, however, Sir Ronald Ross established the *Anopheles* mosquito as the carrier of malaria, following the discoveries of other insect-borne infections. The medical world became more willing to listen to new ideas in this direction.

Now came Dr. Henry R. Carter of the United States Public Health Service, whose original observations raised the curtain on the well-known story of Walter Reed and the discovery of the source and means of controlling yellow fever.

Carter had served many years as a quarantine officer, and he had noticed that, when a seaman developed yellow fever aboard ship, others living with him in the crowded forecastle did not usually have it until some time after he had recovered or died. Carter found a chance to do a statistical study of the spread of yellow fever within families and neighborhoods during an epidemic in Mississippi in 1898. He again observed that persons living with a yellow-fever patient did not get the disease until two or three weeks after the first case had appeared.

No wonder the spread of yellow fever was so mysterious. The chain of infection contained a break in time. Carter called it the "extrinsic incubation" period, meaning that the disease brooded some place in the environment between cases. He did not claim to know where, but carefully made his statistical and tables analysis and sent this original contribution to an American medical journal. His manuscript came back, rejected as being "too long."

Carter was transferred to Havana as quarantine officer at the end of the Spanish-American War in 1898. Finlay was already there. Now the full cast of Act I in the great scientific drama of yellow fever began to assemble. The same year, Major William C. Gorgas reported for duty in Havana and soon became chief sanitary officer for the Army.

The war against Spain, although long for the Cuban patriots, was fortunately brief for the United States. American deaths totaled approximately 2,450; 385 died in battle; yellow fever took 230; the rest died of other diseases.

Dr. Gorgas, then forty-four years old, had a number of distinctions. He was an Alabaman, had been rejected for West Point, had trained under William H. Welch at Bellevue Medical College in New York, was known to the ladies on the Army posts as the "Gorgeous Doctor," and was immune to yellow fever. He had recovered from it during an epidemic at Fort Brown, Texas.

When he arrived in Havana, Gorgas was as ignorant as anyone else of the etiology of yellow fever. Indeed, he believed it to be a filth disease, transmitted by *fomites* (Latin for "tinder," meaning the clothing and bedding of patients, or any substance regarded as capable of transmitting contagion).

Havana, thanks to Spanish oppression and the war, had become a huge cesspool. Dead animals and the sick lay in its stinking streets, otherwise distinguished by orphan children and beggars wandering about homeless—plus flocks of black vultures. Yellow fever had temporarily burned itself out when Gorgas began work under orders to clean up the city. With characteristic efficiency, he did a magnificent job of it in the next two years. The American press printed "before and after" stories and pictures. The great quiet killers, typhoid and dysentery, retreated.

But in 1900, following the arrival of several thousand susceptible Spanish immigrants, yellow fever became epidemic again. Havanese laughed at Gorgas's clean-up, for yellow jack struck, not in the filthy native huts, whose inhabitants seemed immune, but in the more sanitary sections of the city. Prominent American officers died of it; the wife of one, who had thrown herself across her husband's body as he ebbed away in the midst of *vomito negro*, attended his funeral and then went home and killed herself with his revolver. Gorgas's answer was to keep calm and clean harder, while the clerks at Camp Columbia, near Havana, burned sulphur candles at their desks to ward off infection and the officers at mess drank a toast: "Here's to the ones who have gone. Here's to the next one to go."

Surgeon General George Sternberg appointed Major Walter Reed (1851-1902), curator of the Army Medical Museum in Washington, to head a detachment to investigate the causes of yellow fever and other infectious diseases in Cuba. Dr. Reed, then going on fifty years old, was from Virginia. He had studied under Welch at Bellevue and later at Johns Hopkins. He had served at his share of Army posts but preferred bacteriology.

His detachment became known as the United States Army Yellow Fever Board, or Commission; it would now be called a task force or research team. Three others were assigned to it: Dr. James Carroll (1854-1907) of England, Reed's self-effacing assistant at the Museum; Dr. Jesse W. Lazear (1866-1900), also a Southern physician who had studied mosquito transmission of malaria, and was in charge of the Las Animas Hospital Laboratory at Camp Columbia, and Dr. Aristides Agramonte (1869-1931), son of a Cuban patriot, a classmate of Lazear at the College of Physicians and Surgeons in New York, and a yellow-fever specialist in charge of the laboratory at Military Hospital No. 1 in Havana. Agramonte was apparently immune to yellow fever.

The cast was now complete, and by June 25, 1900, all were in Cuba, including Gorgas, Finlay, and Carter.

The story has been told and retold from various viewpoints. Laying them side by side, one finds certain discrepancies and inconsistencies that may never be reconciled. It is doubtful that in a period of only six months the scientific knowledge of many diseases has taken a bigger leap forward. Indeed, what happened in 1900 and 1901 set the pattern of attempts to control yellow fever for the next thirty years. In instances of literary conflict, we have accepted the eyewitness account of Agramonte as the most useful for the brief recapitulation that follows.

Reed and Carroll saw their first case of yellow fever the day they arrived at Las Animas Hospital, Camp Columbia. The Army's chief surgeon in Cuba was in bed with it. In the eighteen clinical cases and eleven autopsies that they studied in the next month or so, the four investigators first tried to find *Salmonella icteroides*, a bacterium that had been suggested as the cause of yellow fever. Reed concluded, correctly, that it was not.

Reed pondered the next step. Thanks to Lazear, he could not overlook the mosquito possibility. He talked to Finlay, who was pleased to have someone besides his wife and assistant listen to him. Carter, a fellow Virginian, came to see Reed and showed him his Mississippi study on the extrinsic incubation period. Always, there was this lag averaging twelve days between the first appearance and second wave of yellow fever.

"Are you sure your dates are accurate?" Reed insisted.

Carter was sure.

"Then it spells an insect host," said Reed. Ross had found this same time break in mosquito transmission of malaria.

On August 1, the Board came to a decision. It would

repeat Finlay's discredited experiment of having his mosquitoes bite yellow-fever patients and then normal persons. Finlay gave them some aegypti eggs to hatch. Unfortunately Reed, during the first week of August, went back to Washington to finish a report, "Typhoid Fever in the Army." This was a handicap, for the four had agreed that they would work not as individuals but as a team; without a leader on the spot, this would be harder to do.

It was agreed, however, that Lazear should be the mosquito man, and in due time he had larvae and then adult mosquitoes and later their eggs and larvae to work with. He put each female in a labeled test tube with a wad of gauze stuffed in the top to keep her from flying away. Lazear then fed his mosquitoes on yellow-fever patients and, with his colleagues, proceeded to expose nine volunteers to the (hopefully) infected mosquitoes. The human guinea pigs, mainly soldiers around the hospital, were skeptical about their chance of getting yellow fever and became more so as failures piled up. Whoever was on hand routinely fed the non-exposed mosquitoes by pulling the stopper and clapping the test tube on his forearm. The mosquito, if hungry, would light on the skin and stick her beak into a capillary.

The Board members had agreed that they would accept the same risks as any other volunteer. But Reed was away and Agramonte was immune. On August 16, Lazear exposed himself to a mosquito that ten days before had sampled a yellow-fever patient in his fifth day of illness. Nothing happened. The team still had to learn that a yellow-fever patient is only infectious during the first three days or so of his illness—when the virus is circulating in his blood stream.

They were discouraged. It took an accident to get

them moving. On August 27, Lazear spent the morning feeding his mosquitoes; one, that on August 15 had fed on a patient in his second day of illness, would not eat. Lazear in the afternoon mentioned this to Carroll, who thought he might try to feed the insect; it looked weak and tired. Lazear and Carroll held the mosquito's tube on the latter's forearm for some time before it bit him.

Two days later, Carroll did not feel well. On the next day, August 30, he had chills and fever. When Agramonte and then Gorgas came to see him, he was tossing restlessly in bed, in high fever, his eyes bloodshot, on the verge of a delirium that soon followed. It was a familiar sight—yellow fever. The disease ran a rough course, but fortunately did not end in black vomit. Carroll's eyeballs turned saffron yellow. In a week he was out of danger and on the mend. It was their first success; the overriding scientific question, however, was whether this particular mosquito's bite or something else had brought on the disease.

"We decided to test it upon the first non-immune person who should offer himself to be bitten," wrote Agramonte. Within fifteen minutes of the two doctors' decision a soldier came by the laboratory door, saluted, and stopped to watch Lazear coaxing a mosquito from one test tube to another.

"You still fooling with mosquitoes, Doctor?"

"Yes, will you take a bite?"

"Sure, I ain't scared of 'em," said the man, who was William H. Dean of Troop B, Seventh Cavalry.

Lazear looked at Agramonte, who nodded his head.

Five days from the time Dean bared his arm to the mosquito he came down with yellow fever. He was their first purely experimental case. Happily, he recovered.

Agramonte and Lazear cabled Reed the good news. They also agreed, in view of Carroll's narrow escape, that one hero on the Board was enough; they had the scientific work to do and it served no purpose to take further risks.

On September 18, Lazear admitted to feeling out of sorts and stayed in quarters. That night he had a chill and the next day he had all the signs of a severe attack of yellow fever. Agramonte and Carroll, who was still weak but up and around, questioned Lazear and he assured them he had *not* experimented on himself with one of the test-tube mosquitoes. What had happened, he said, was this: Five days before, he had been holding a test tube with a mosquito upon a man's abdomen in Las Animas Hospital, and another insect flying about the room came to rest on his hand. He was tempted to brush it off, but did not want to move lest he disturb the insect feeding inside the tube's mouth, so he allowed the stray mosquito to have its fill, thinking he would then capture it. But the mosquito flew away. Reed later suspected that Lazear had conducted an experiment with a labeled mosquito without the knowledge of his colleagues and then made up his story. Reed, in any event, let it stand as an "accident in line of duty."

Gorgas said Lazear's was one of the most terrible cases he had ever seen, ending in wild delirium and black vomit. It took two men to hold Lazear in bed as he died the morning of September 25, 1900.

Reed returned to Havana in early October and he, Agramonte, and Carroll agreed that three cases, the first open to some question and the third "accidental," were not enough to convince others. What they needed was a better controlled series.

In October, they constructed Camp Lazear, in a

secluded spot some distance from Camp Columbia. In November and December, they conducted two types of experiment. In the first, they intimately exposed seven susceptible American volunteers to the soiled and bloody clothing, towels, and bedding of yellow-fever patients for twenty consecutive nights, a nauseating experience that proved people did not catch the disease from "fomites." In the second, eleven of the thirteen volunteers (mostly Spanish immigrants who were paid) acquired yellow fever from the bites of infected mosquitoes.

The cause was something that the mosquito passed from one person's blood to another, but what? Efforts to see the yellow-fever germ under the microscope, cultivate it under glass, or transmit it to an experimental animal failed.

Reed and Carroll returned to Washington. The following summer Welch called Reed's attention to the discovery of Friedrich A. J. Loeffler (1852-1915) and Paul Frosch (1860-1928), both Germans, in 1898, that foot-and-mouth disease in cattle is transmitted by a filtrate of infected blood serum that has been forced several times through a porcelain filter capable of stopping the smallest known bacterium or other living cell.

Reed sent Carroll back to Havana in August 1901 to make this experiment with yellow fever. Carroll found Dr. Juan Guiteras (1852-1925), the Havana health officer, engaged in immunization experiments. Guiteras had noted that all the yellow-fever cases had been mild in the Yellow Fever Commission's second series of mosquito-transmitted cases. He was reminded that in the eighteenth century, before Edward Jenner (1749-1823) of England introduced his cowpox vaccine against smallpox, it had been the fashion to immunize people by inoculating them with matter from a "mild case" of smallpox. He tried to do this with yellow-fever infected mosquitoes. The results were disastrous. Three of eight volunteers died.

Carroll, in October, infected a Spaniard with one of Guiteras's mosquitoes. Carroll drew blood from the patient, carefully filtered the serum, and injected the filtrate in three American volunteers. One had a mild fever and headache, but two developed clear-cut yellow fever (and survived).

Reed and Carroll concluded that they were dealing with a micro-organism so small that it could not be trapped in the finest filter, or be seen under a microscope, much as Pasteur had postulated an ultramicroscopic agent as the cause of rabies.

They did not use the term "filterable virus." It came into use later. They did not know that they were dealing with a spherical particle measuring from one to two millionths of an inch in diameter and, like the living-cell nucleus, largely made up of nucleic acid and proteins. Finlay, who had been inclined to find fault with the Yellow Fever Commission's work, interpreted Carroll's experiments as a failure to find the yellow-fever germ in the patient's blood. He said that the search must go on.

Reed—he would die in another year from appendicitis and be followed four years later by Carroll, dead of heart disease—now tossed the ball to sanitarian Gorgas. Gorgas had looked on the Las Animas and Camp Lazear experiments with some reservation and doubt.

"If it is the mosquito," he said stoutly, "I am going to get rid of the mosquito."

"It can't be done," said Reed.

All they had to do was look around. There were millions of mosquitoes in the Havana air. Anyway, how

could anyone be sure that only aegypti mosquitoes carried yellow fever, that other insects or animals might not
also carry it?

Gorgas began his Havana campaign early in 1901
as an attack on all mosquitoes, using shotgun methods.
Later, he attributed his good results mainly to two measures, the placing of yellow-fever patients in isolation
and the killing of adult mosquitoes. Every reported yellow-fever patient was put in a tightly screened room
during his infective period and the room was afterward
fumigated to kill infected mosquitoes.

His conclusion was incorrect. By luck, he also introduced the method most certain to bring *Aëdes aegypti*
to its doom: a house-to-house attack on its breeding
places. Gorgas's mosquito hunters found aegypti mosquitoes breeding in barrels, jugs, vases, and so on. He
obtained a ruling from the Havana City Council that
every water container in the city would have to be
emptied, completely covered, or a thin layer of kerosene
would be poured on the water's surface to kill the mosquito larvae. And, said the Council, any householder
found to be breeding mosquitoes on his premises would
be fined ten dollars, a large sum.)

Thus began a gigantic game between Gorgas's staff
of inspectors and the people of Havana who removed
or hid their water containers every time the inspector
came down the street. But the inspectors anticipated
evasion; they counted every container down to the last
pitcher and listed each in a card index. The housewife
had to produce everything listed, or account for it. If it
was uncovered and contained water, in went some kerosene to suffocate the wigglers.

Havanese laughed at the Yankees. It was a great
joke to see them send the inspectors around once a month

to every house, hotel, barroom, and building, and then play hide-and-seek with pots and jugs. The owner had a choice of installing plumbing, of course. Latin tempers flared; voices were raised. But nobody got hurt. Gorgas was good-humored, polite, tactful, and spoke Spanish. He rarely fined anyone, but he was an absolute colossus of system and hard work. He licked yellow fever in Havana with a mildness of manner and passion for detail.

For 140 years—from 1762 to 1901—Havana had not seen a day without a report of yellow fever. Gorgas launched his campaign in March and by the following October no more yellow fever was being reported. During that time, there were just six cases. There were none in the next nine months. Except for one outbreak in 1905 that was quickly vanquished with the methods Gorgas had introduced, yellow-fever epidemics became a thing of the past in Havana. It was unbelievable that a disease so deeply implanted could be uprooted only a year after it killed Lazear. Aegypti mosquitoes did not totally disappear, but many a beaming señora would reassure the mosquito inspector when he rang the front doorbell: *"No hay mosquitos aqui, señor."* (We have no mosquitoes here, sir.)

Dr. Oswaldo Cruz (1872-1917) of Brazil confirmed this anti-mosquito approach by going ahead and wiping yellow fever out of Rio de Janeiro by 1908. Only gradually did the mosquito hunters become convinced that the house mosquito, *Aëdes aegypti*, was the only transmitter of urban yellow fever and, since it bred around the house, was a target for rifle-shot methods.

Gorgas visualized what he had to do next and got busy. Theodore Roosevelt had become President and was getting ready to build the Panama Canal, cutting through years of speculative, economic, political, and diplomatic manipulation and intrigue in Rough Rider style. Ever since Balboa crossed the fifty-mile Isthmus of Panama from the Atlantic to the Pacific in 1513, the world had been waiting for somebody to dig a shipping canal there. Roosevelt was determined to do it. Ferdinand de Lesseps (1805-1894) and his stockholders, the people of France, had made two efforts to build a Panama canal, starting in 1881, and had made a mess of it each time. There had been much graft and mismanagement, but Gorgas knew what really defeated De Lesseps: yellow fever and malaria.

Gorgas told Surgeon General Sternberg that mosquitoes were the greatest obstacle to building the canal, and convinced him. He said the project would need an experienced sanitarian in charge, "and I should like to be that man." In one of those happy instances in which the right man not only wanted the job but got it, Gorgas was appointed chief sanitary officer of the Panama Canal Zone and promoted to colonel in 1902. But it wasn't until the spring of 1904 that, in Teddy Roosevelt's words, "the dirt started to fly." Meanwhile Gorgas investigated the problem to be solved, traveling to France and the Suez Canal, where De Lesseps had succeeded, but without yellow fever and with only a small amount of malaria to bother his workers.

Gorgas found that the French company had concealed the extent of sickness and death they had faced in the Isthmus of Panama from 1881 to 1889. He verified his impression when he arrived in Panama in March 1904. He saw the "Folie Dingler," the $150,000 mansion that the chief engineer, Jules Dingler, had built in 1884 for his wife, son, daughter, and her fiancé, only to see them all die of yellow fever; Dingler himself returned to France a broken man, and soon died.

Thousands of Frenchmen were buried in a place called Monkey Hill. In the wet season, from April to December, sometimes thirty or forty a day had died, week after week. From such data as Gorgas could find he estimated that in eight years the French lost some 20,000, or a third, of their imported workers, including Europeans and Chinese.

Surprisingly, the United States government in its planning did not recognize disease as any great obstacle. This was a civil engineer's job, and engineers are practical-minded people. They get the job done. The French had created such a financial scandal, the prime objective of the first chairman of the Panama Canal Commission was to save money. He knew all about Walter Reed's work in Havana and regarded it as a lot of nonsense. He saw the Sanitary Department as of about the same importance as street cleaning. Gorgas's job was to tidy up Colon and Panama City and get rid of the smells.

The Isthmus of Panama was not only the battleground for the fulfillment of the mariner's dream of a short cut to the South Pacific but also, and of far greater importance to humanity, of medical science's final repudiation of the miasma-and-filth theories of infectious disease.

Yellow fever was quiet when Gorgas arrived but cases began coming in to the Ancon Hospital not long after the first load of non-immune workers got off the boat. There was a small epidemic in November 1904. The chief engineer, who had brought a coffin with him in case he needed it, resigned and went home, touching off a mass urge to leave before it was too late. For the thousands of workers there was no way back. They saw nothing in their future but a grave on Monkey Hill.

It was a sort of last, wry, tragic tribute to Benja-

min Rush that, in the minds of high officials on the Canal
Commission, the stench caused yellow fever. In a few
instances, they were backed up by prominent American
physicians and at one time the chairman of the Commission tried to replace Gorgas with an osteopath.

Gorgas, however, already had made the "let's-clean-
up" mistake in Havana, and in his gentle, patient, but
determined way, did not propose to make it again. His
superiors at first prevented him from fighting mosquitoes and then held him responsible for the epidemic
because his clean-up efforts were inadequate. Secretary
of War William H. Taft visited the Canal Zone during
the fall epidemic and returned to Washington determined
to get rid of Gorgas. The Commission and the governor
of the Canal Zone were in full accord. Gorgas must go.

Taft so recommended to the President at least
twice, but Roosevelt sought the counsel of friends high
in American medicine, such as Welch, and they reassured him he had the best man he could get—let him
fight mosquitoes.

The American Medical Association conducted its
own investigation and became an effective counter-
critic. While the Commission was agitating to get rid
of everyone who wanted to fight mosquitoes, the
A.M.A. published an exposé of the Commission's ignorance and incompetence. Roosevelt responded by fir-
ing all seven members of the Commission.

Gorgas suffered almost continuous criticism, interference, and obstruction for the first two or three
years. Yet he was the only high official who lasted out the
nine-year period of construction and saw, as the product
of his own presence, the first ship go through the Canal
in August 1914.

Gorgas managed to get his fight against *Aëdes*

aegypti organized in early 1905. It was Havana all over again. By the following year yellow fever appeared, incredibly enough, to be a thing of the past in Panama, too.)

Gorgas understood precisely what he, with the help of men like Carter, had accomplished. (They had made the Panama Canal possible. It is no wonder that the yellow-fever-mosquito experts in the next few years became a group of positive thinkers, aware they were making history and eager to finish the job. Their mood may be gathered from the occasion when a doctor friend asked Gorgas, who was Surgeon General of the Army during World War I, the first thing he would do if he received a telephone call that the war had ended:

"Do you know what I would do?" said Gorgas. "I would ring off, call New York City, and order a passage for South America. I would go to Guayaquil, Ecuador, the only place in which yellow fever is prevalent, exterminate the pestilence, and then—and then return to Panama, the garden spot of the world, and end my days writing an elegy on yellow fever.")

22

Civilizing the Tropics

Gorgas believed the tropics, as beautiful as they are savage, to be the original center of civilization. He saw such diseases as yellow fever and malaria as barriers to the return of a society of educated and industrious men to the torrid zones of Latin America and Africa. He conceived it as his mission to conquer yellow fever and so get the materialization of this dream of a developing tropics under way.

Frederick Gates and Wickliffe Rose, with their own dream of conquering disease and improving rural health throughout the world, saw to it that Gorgas was elected to the commission of the International Health Division in June 1913, at its first meeting. In 1914, Gorgas became Army Surgeon General. He was one of the first men Rose wanted to see when he returned from a trip around the world.

Rose told Gorgas that the British Medical Service in India was in a state of "great anxiety" about what would happen when the Panama Canal opened that fall. India and other countries of the Far East had no yellow fever. Their health officials feared that the opening of trade routes through the Canal would bring them yellow fever for the first time.

Rose pointed out that the Panama Canal was undertaken in the interest of civilization. "Naturally," he said, "we are interested in the new sanitary responsibilities growing out of it. . . . What, if anything, might be undertaken with promise of definite and lasting results?"

"The control of yellow fever," Gorgas replied.

Rose, Gorgas, and the two Public Health Service yellow-fever experts, Drs. Henry R. Carter and Joseph H. White, talked yellow-fever prevention at various times. Out of their discussions came Rose's memorandum "Yellow Fever: Feasibility of Its Eradication" (October 27, 1914).

Gorgas had not the slightest doubt that yellow fever could be promptly wiped out. By this time, it had been done in Havana, Panama, Rio de Janeiro, and Vera Cruz. As Rose put the recipe in writing: "We have simply to remove from the home premises all receptacles which contain or may contain clear water long enough to breed these mosquitoes. Where removal of such containers is impossible other measures such as screening to prevent their use as breeding places may be adopted. This is the whole task; nothing else need be done."

Carter had developed the seed-bed, or key-center, theory of the spread of yellow fever. He believed that yellow fever could maintain itself continuously only in a few sizable port cities with an influx of non-immune children and newcomers sufficient to keep the virus going around in mosquitoes. The disease might travel forth from these centers and circle the world, but it was these seed beds that perpetuated it. When aegypti mosquitoes could be found in fewer than 5 percent of the houses in an endemic area and the disease ceased to spread, the virus would die out.

To Gorgas's knowledge, the worst yellow-fever pesthole in the world was Guayaquil, in Ecuador, on the west coast of South America, about three and a half days by boat from Panama. No ship from Guayaquil was permitted to dock in Panama until the end of the sixth day out. Eradication of yellow fever in Guayaquil would bring these ports two and a half days closer together.

Other known or suspected foci of yellow fever were, in Yucatán: Merida and Campeche; in Brazil: Manaus, Recife, Salvador, and Belem do Para; in Venezuela: La Guaira, and possibly some other ports on the south shore of the Caribbean; in Africa: various ports on the west coast from Sierra Leone to the Gulf of Guinea. "I should be in favor of making a start at Guayaquil and Manaus," Gorgas commented. "Guayaquil first and Manaus second. But I would feel great confidence that yellow fever would disappear of itself after we once got Manaus and Guayaquil under control."

There was discussion about how long yellow-fever eradication would take. Carter estimated that to organize a mosquito program and get it working efficiently would take three to six months, and to finish the work would take from three to four months more—in other words, from six to ten months over all.

Gorgas agreed that with a free hand a program director could finish the job in Guayaquil (population: 80,000) in six months but, because of the desirability of making a small beginning and then expanding, and to allow for delays, he would set two years as a safe time limit.

Cooperation was a bridge they would have to cross.

"Ecuador, we are told, and especially the people of Guayaquil, do not like Americans," remarked Rose. "Whether or not the city would contribute funds, grant the necessary authority, or even permit the work to be undertaken remains to be ascertained."

In May 1915, the Rockefeller Foundation declared itself "prepared to give aid in the eradication of this disease." In June 1916, Gorgas headed a six-man Yellow Fever Commission that left for South America and a six-month investigation of the whereabouts of yellow fever. The Commission reported that insofar as it could determine "the only endemic center for yellow fever in South America at present is Guayaquil."

The International Health Division received Gorgas's report and recommendations for the eradication of yellow fever from Guayaquil early in 1917 and appointed him director of its yellow-fever-control program. It expressed the hope that it would be his privilege to write the last chapter in the history of yellow fever. America's entrance into World War I and his duties as Surgeon General of the Army made it impossible, however, for him to begin the campaign until 1918.

When the opportunity came, the Ecuadorians, far from being hostile to the Yankees, welcomed them and the result was another triumph over yellow fever. Dr. Michael E. Connor (1879-1941), a member of the I.H.D. field staff, was in immediate charge of the 125 inspectors organized in twenty-five anti-mosquito squads who started operations in Guayaquil in December 1918. There had been a more-than-average amount of yellow fever in the famous old pest-hole that summer. The disease during the previous eight years had averaged 259 cases annually. Connor concentrated on the mosquito-proofing of water tanks, the putting of larva-eating fish in the cisterns and other containers, and detecting and destroying mosquito larvae by means of weekly house inspections.

The last case of yellow fever in Guayaquil was reported in May 1919, only six months after control work had started. It was Havana all over again. In 1920, Panama lifted its quarantine against ships from Guayaquil. Urban yellow fever departed, not only from the seaport but seemingly from most of Ecuador.

This seemed to confirm the key-center theory.

There was one source of distraction. Yellow fever had broken out on the west coast of Guatemala in June 1918, producing 550 cases and 200 deaths. The International Health Division sent White down and he had the epidemic under control by September.

In 1919 and 1920, however, yellow fever broke out in Peru, Brazil, Honduras, Salvador, Mexico, Nicaragua, and Guatemala again. There were no key centers, strictly speaking; it now seemed that there were more keys on the ring than Gorgas thought.

He wanted to investigate West Africa. Yellow fever had been suspected there, but nobody knew much about it. In 1920, the I.H.D. appointed the Yellow Fever Commission to the West Coast of Africa.

The six-man commission was to sail for Africa from London. But Gorgas, then sixty-six years old, collapsed in London and died some days later, on July 4, 1920. He was at first thought to have suffered a stroke, but kidney disease was later believed to be the cause of death. His mind remained clear during this final period, in which he knew he would die, and therefore he had some appreciation of the fact that the entire civilized world, as it were, was watching over him. This was signalized when King George came to his bedside and knighted him. One of world health's great heroes died a royal death.

The Commission had sailed on June 30 without its leader, and spent fifteen weeks visiting the Belgian Congo, Dahomey, Gold Coast, Senegal, Sierra Leone, and Nigeria. "No authentic case of yellow fever was seen," but apparently it had been present in recent years, the Commission reported. It encountered a deeply rooted native habit of concealing all cases of sickness. The region was vast, travel difficult, and living conditions primitive. It did not appear that pursuants of the key-center theory would have an easy time of it in Africa.

23

"Funny Noguchi"

We have not mentioned the Japanese doctor Hideyo Noguchi (1876-1928) in Guayaquil. A separate story, one of the most fantastic misadventures in medical research, began there in July 1918, before Connor controlled the mosquitoes. Noguchi drew a gigantic red herring across the yellow-fever trail and it took ten years to remove it. Gorgas engineered the project, but did not live to see its outcome. Rose, who had faith in Noguchi, moved on, and so it was Frederick Russell who eventually had to weather the tragedy as director of the International Health Division. Three yellow-fever fighters paid with their lives for the new knowledge gained. Noguchi lived long enough to realize that he had made the commonest mistake in medicine: a wrong diagnosis.

The issue was "What causes yellow fever?"

While James Carroll provided evidence that a filterable virus transmitted from one human being to another by the bite of *Aëdes aegypti* mosquitoes was the cause of yellow fever, he did not meet all the requirements of proof that bacteriologists were accustomed to. He did not see the organism under a microscope, grow it in "pure culture," or experimentally produce the same disease with it by passage through laboratory animals. The postulates of the German Robert Koch (1843-1910) of what constitutes proof require that the scientist single out the specific germ from all those that might be competing with it for etiological honors. Limitation of evidence to two or three human experiments was handicapping. It would have helped if Carroll had been able to transmit his hypothetical ultramicrobe from one guinea pig, monkey, or other laboratory animal to another. Such experiments were attempted without success.

Several others appeared to have confirmed Carroll's discovery that the cause of yellow fever, whatever it was, passed through the finest Berkefeld filters. Closely examined, however, the evidence was not massive or incontrovertible, and in any event left the question of the germ's identity unanswered.

If Gorgas was going to rid the world of yellow fever, as he intended, it would be helpful to know what he was talking about—to be able to answer such questions as: What is yellow fever? What is not yellow fever? In the tropics, as elsewhere, there are a variety of infectious fevers. In mild cases, many tend to look alike. Even when serious, some are apt to behave in the same way—for example, produce the jaundice, protein in urine, and tiny multiple hemorrhages that characterize yellow fever. Ryukichi Inada (1874-1950) and his associates in Japan had isolated the cause of a disease like this just a few years before. Clinically it had been known as Weil's disease—for Adolf Weil (1848-1916) of Germany, who identified it in patients. The two Japanese called Weil's disease "spirochetal jaundice," having found a spirochete, *Leptospira icterohemorrhagiae*, to be the cause.

Equally important, Gorgas saw that answers to such fundamental questions were needed to develop a quick laboratory test for yellow fever (still needed in 1969). He apparently shared the belief of Fritz R. Schaudinn (1871-1906) of Germany, who had discovered the spirochete of syphilis, that another species of these slim, spiral-shaped animacules would prove to be the cause of yellow fever. Noguchi of the Rockefeller Institute for Medical Research, himself a spirochete man, was also disposed to this view.

The I.H.D. appointed a Commission to Study Yellow Fever in Ecuador and made Dr. Arthur I. Kendall, dean of Northwestern University Medical School, its chairman. Gorgas asked Kendall who they should get to do the bacteriology and Kendall replied: "We need Noguchi."

Dr. Hideyo Noguchi had risen to world fame as a bacteriologist on Simon Flexner's original staff at the Rockefeller Institute for Medical Research. He had flung his net widely in studies of snake venom, syphilis, rabies, poliomyelitis, trachoma, Rocky Mountain spotted fever, and hog cholera, but was best known for his research in syphilis. He claimed to have cultivated *Treponema pallidum*, the spirochete of syphilis, in a test tube; others were unable to repeat his results. He also claimed to have cultivated the organisms causing rabies, polio, and trachoma, but this work never was confirmed either.

It was not difficult for the Rockefeller Foundation to borrow Noguchi from the Rockefeller Institute. He had just recovered from a long bout with typhoid fever, was at loose ends, and was looking for new worlds to conquer. Noguchi was habitually looking for new worlds to conquer.

Born of a servant family in Japan, and first called Seisaku Noguchi, the young man attracted the attention of teachers, who never were quite sure whether he was a genius or just crazy. He had a consuming ambition "to accomplish the impossible," as he said. This led one of his professors to suggest he change his first name to Hideyo, meaning "great man of the world." While in medical school in Tokyo, he determined that somehow he would get to Germany for training, but decided to go by way of the United States, where he brought himself to the attention of Flexner, then at the University of Pennsylvania.

Noguchi had a nearly unlimited capacity for work, day and night, and by the time the Rockefeller Institute opened in 1904 had shown great promise. Those who knew him as a fiercely aloof, solitary figure gathered he suffered from a sense of inferiority because of his left hand, almost fingerless from burns as a baby; his poor English, corrected in his many scientific papers by helpful editors, and his small stature. But his chief characteristics appeared to be a towering egocentricity—he insisted on working alone—and a winsome manner. His friends and assistants idolized him. He often spoke of himself as "funny Noguchi," as if quoting the opinion of others.

Guayaquil, as mentioned earlier, was having a more than usual amount of yellow fever when Noguchi arrived in July 1918. He brought a staggering amount of laboratory paraphernalia, as on all his expeditions to come. He wore puttees with his street clothes—to protect his legs from the mosquitoes, he said. He brought sixty guinea pigs with him, in a South American adaptation of "carrying coals to Newcastle." The mountains of Ecuador are the home of the guinea pigs.

Technically, Noguchi and his guinea pigs should not have been allowed in Ecuador, for the country had laws against the admission of Japanese and guinea pigs. Such laws officials in Guayaquil graciously overlooked. They were eager to relieve their city of its pesthole reputation.

By importing his favorite laboratory animal, Noguchi got off to a fast start. He had been there only nine days, working in his usual secretive way, embarrassing American and Ecuadorean doctors alike, when he called Kendall to the microscope and said: "Look in there. That is the one I suspect." Within a month Noguchi told Guayaquil newspapers that he had found the presumable cause of yellow fever, and a few days later added that he had transmitted it to guinea pigs.

Of course, it was a spirochete. There is an aphorism in medical science which says: "You see what you look for; you look for what you know." It can work positively or negatively. If you know something exists but is hidden from view, you may be able to espy clues that thereafter will lead you to it. Thus, discoveries in diagnostic method may be made. On the other hand, if you know something exists in some instances and generalize it to be of significance in all, you may be right—or you may gravely mislead yourself and others.

After four months' work in Ecuador, Noguchi went back to New York and wrote a series of fourteen reports subsequently published in the *Journal of Experimental Medicine*. It would take his critics another six years to flank this Maginot Line of publications and nine years to destroy his defenses in one final blitzkrieg.

Noguchi began by analyzing 172 cases diagnosed as yellow fever in the Yellow Fever Hospital at Guayaquil. He injected the blood of twenty-seven patients into seventy-four "g-pigs." From six patients he got eight takes—that is, the guinea pigs came down with "symptoms resembling human yellow fever." In the case of "A. Ce.," an eighteen-year-old seamstress who died of an apparent classic yellow fever on the seventh day, following black vomit, he saw under his dark-field microscope a small number of spirochetes. He cultivated this organism, and established a line of infection in twenty-seven g-pigs. Not all died, but eight did; some only sickened; others remained well.

Noguchi called his spirochete *Leptospira icteroides.* He said that it was closely related to the *Leptospira icterohemorrhagiae* found by Inada to be the cause of Weil's disease, but immunologically distinct. Carter came to see him in New York and questioned him closely on this point. Carter said he knew how easy it was during an epidemic to mistake Weil's disease for yellow fever. Noguchi said his germ produced a different kind of immunity and Carter took his word for it.

When Noguchi spoke, bacteriology listened—except Dr. Mario G. Lebredo, the Cuban member of the Commission. Lebredo told Noguchi that he was confusing yellow fever with Weil's disease. Hadn't Noguchi himself found that 60 percent of the rats that shared the living quarters of people in Guayaquil carried *Leptospira icterohemorrhagiae?* If this was true, was it not likely there would be some Weil's disease occurring among human beings at the same time there was yellow fever? It was also most unusual that he had been able to transmit "yellow fever" to dogs. It was not a canine disease.

Certainly, there was some cause for reserving judgment in the fact that Noguchi could find *Leptospira* in only a few, rather than most, of the alleged yellow-fever patients, and further that, even when he established the germ in guinea pigs, it did not perform consistently.

On the other hand, he claimed that his spirochete would pass through Berkefeld filters, just as Reed's filterable virus did. It just took longer and fewer got through, that was all. Furthermore, he also showed that aegypti mosquitoes would transmit his yellow fever from human patients to guinea pigs, if 100 to 300 mosquitoes were allowed to bite first patients and then guinea pig. True, he only got two positive takes in thirteen experiments. Havana mosquitoes had been much more efficient in human experiments.

In total effect, however, Noguchi was saying what his audience wanted to hear. There was no time for doubts. He had isolated, seen, cultivated, and transmitted a spirochete that caused a yellow fever, and had a remedy at hand. Working at a furious pace, Noguchi before his return to New York developed both a vaccine and an immune serum that, as he saw it, showed immediate promise in the prevention and treatment of yellow fever.

All the early reports from clinical trials of the vaccine were good. These came from various places in Central and South America and Noguchi combined them in his reports. The serum, if given before the third day after onset of symptoms, was said to reduce the mortality rate from yellow fever from 50 or 60 down to 9 percent.

The vaccine was first tested in Guayaquil, at the suggestion of Governor Pareja. There was to be a national celebration in the city in October 1918, and some "vincedores" soldiers and their families were to be sent down from Quito, the capital, to participate. Meanwhile yellow fever was occurring at the rate of two or three cases a day. Noguchi vaccinated 325 soldiers and members of their families, allowing at least ten days for the vaccination to give protection. To these he added another 102 persons vaccinated at various later times, for a total of 427. Yellow fever eventually struck five of them. For comparison, Noguchi used the yellow-fever cases reported in Guayaquil from October through March—a total of 386—over a base of 3,573 "non-immunes" selected from a population of about 80,000 (the majority of whom, it might be guessed, were already immune). As computed, the yellow-fever incidence rates were 11 per 1,000 for the vaccinated group against 110 per 1,000 for the unvaccinated.

How Noguchi arrived at his control group he did not say, but his calculations revealed a complete lack of statistical sophistication, even for his day. One of many who later pored over the early figures, trying to make sense of them, was Dr. Wilbur A. Sawyer, who became director of the Foundation's Yellow Fever Laboratory in New York in 1928. Sawyer found that the figures in Noguchi's vaccination articles did not pass the simplest statistical test. He remarked that Noguchi's associates seemed to lose all faculty for scientific criticism in his presence. The figures were generally accepted at the time, however, with the exception of a number of Cuban physicians who had seen a lot of yellow fever and sensed discrepancies.

Yellow-fever epidemics continued to break out in various parts of Latin America—Peru had 15,000 to 20,000 cases in 1920-1921.

Noguchi was able to confirm *Leptospira icteroides* as the agent of yellow fever in Peru, Mexico, and Brazil. Others sometimes got his results; sometimes they didn't.

He encountered no serious challenge until 1924. Then, at the Myrtle Bank Hotel in Kingston, Jamaica, Aristides Agramonte, the only survivor of the original

Reed study group, confronted him. The occasion was the International Conference on Health Problems in Tropical America. In addition to Agramonte and Noguchi, other greats of tropical medicine and public health were there.

Agramonte rose to make "some observations upon yellow fever prophylaxis," and began by lamenting that so much time was taken up by "the thankless task of setting aside erroneous methods and deductions." The value of the vaccine against yellow fever, he said, could not be shown unless it were proved that the chance of infection was the same for the vaccinated as for those not vaccinated. This had not been the case.

He called Noguchi "the savant" and those who accepted his work "his disciples." When others failed to transmit yellow fever to guinea pigs and dogs, Agramonte pointed out that Noguchi attributed their failures to "faulty technique." This was not fair to some good men who just happened not to agree with him.

Personally, Agramonte could not see any pronounced difference between *Leptospira icterohemorrhagiae* and *L. icteroides*, although Weil's disease and yellow fever themselves were clinically and pathologically "entirely unlike." At best, Noguchi's organism appeared to be a fellow traveler in some cases of yellow fever. If what he said was true, his was the only spirochete transmitted by a mosquito; that seemed improbable. Furthermore, if anything were known about yellow fever, transmission surely did not take place by contact. And yet, using Noguchi's own strain, they had in Havana transmitted the infection from dog to dog by contact. Agramonte challenged Noguchi to attempt to transmit his germ back to a human being "causing thereby an undisputed case of yellow fever."

To speak of a man's work in a scientific circle as Agramonte did, with the subject seated in the circle, was the intellectual equivalent of a public whipping. Of course, Agramonte was now at best a senior statesman and Noguchi was, at forty-eight, in his prime. He could afford to indulge an old man.

Quietly, Noguchi said that there was no intention of replacing anti-mosquito measures with the vaccine and serum, but only to use these as a supplement. He again emphasized "the importance of proper facilities and technical training" in the study of *Leptospira*, and so again offended the Latin Americans who apparently could not see as much through a microscope as a man from the Rockefeller Institute. He claimed the *Leptospira* of Weil's disease and yellow fever showed differences.

Noguchi also got a dressing-down on his statistics, and this time there could be no argument as to who was the more expert. Defending the vaccine, Noguchi presented results from Tuxpan, Mexico, which had a yellow-fever epidemic in the fall of 1920. As an emergency measure, 2,000 persons were vaccinated over a thirty-nine-day period in the middle of the epidemic beginning in August and ending in December. Among the 4,000 remaining unvaccinated were eighty-five cases of yellow fever; among the vaccinated, not a single case—excluding sixteen cases occurring within the first ten days after vaccination, before an immunity had built up.

On the face of it, this evidence sounded convincing, if the treated and untreated groups could be presumed to have been drawn at random from the same population. But Dr. William H. Park (1863-1939), head of the New York City Health Department, subtly demolished Noguchi's evidence on the basis of his own extensive experience.

Park indicated that in a vaccination program carried on during an epidemic there is a kind of stripping action that moves the bulk of cases into the unvaccinated group. To elucidate, about 6,000 were supposedly at risk and none protected at the beginning of vaccination in Tuxpan. In the course of the next six and a half weeks, 2,000 who so far had not come down with yellow fever were subtracted from the 6,000 and placed in the treated group. Thus, the untreated group bore the brunt of yellow fever occurring during that time and the 2,000 vaccinated were tested in total only at the tail end of the epidemic.

It was a bad day for Noguchi.

24

The Truth Can Make You Dead

Despite many outbreaks of yellow fever in South and Central America in the early 1920's, the International Health Division remained bullish about the imminent conquest of yellow fever. Frederick Russell, its chief, believed in yellow fever control as wholly an urban problem, and, as one laboratory man of another, in Noguchi. With only three cases of yellow fever reported in the entire Western Hemisphere in 1925, the news was generally good. "While the fight against yellow fever is drawing to a close in America," Russell wrote in his annual report for 1924, "men are in training and equipment is being assembled for the long-anticipated attack upon its ultimate stronghold—West Africa."

The West Africa Yellow Fever Commission of the I. H. D. now established a well-equipped, well-staffed laboratory at Yaba, near Lagos, the flat, sandy, marshy capital of Nigeria, a city then of approximately 99,000 Africans and 1,000 British. The Commission, actually a field program with a rotating staff, operated from 1925 until 1934 from this base and at times from Accra, a city of 42,000, some 250 miles to the west (then in the Gold Coast, now Ghana).

Russell wanted an Army doctor to direct this second commission to Africa and was happy to get Major Henry Beeuwkes (1881-1956), Johns Hopkins–trained bacteriologist, whom he had known at the Army Medical School in Washington. The remainder of Beeuwkes's professional staff, usually numbering around eight but totaling twenty-four in nine years, will be introduced as we come to them.

Naturally, this being Africa, the Rockefeller group soaked up the hair-raising romance of the Dark Continent and became imbued with the "white man's grave" outlook. Their immediate problem was not yellow fever but malaria. The British did not screen their houses; *Aëdes aegypti* was common though under partial control, but *Anopheles gambiae*, most savage mosquito of them all, was everywhere. Beeuwkes imported six portable houses of asbestos cement from Philadelphia, to be used as laboratory, office, staff bungalows, staff dining hall, and animal house. All these were tightly screened, but one could not stay behind screens for an eighteen-months' tour of duty; as a matter of fact, many of the staff ranged over an area of several hundred miles in depth. They traveled however they could, often by boat, sometimes on foot; but their favorite conveyance was a Dodge touring car.

Beeuwkes had wanted to take a coffin to Lagos, sure that someone would need it. Russell denied the request. They needed several. However, there was no death for the first two years, none at all before they found a new experimental animal.

Most had malaria at one time or another; all took daily quinine. Beeuwkes had malaria continuously for several years, suppressing it with quinine but suffering acute attacks every time he stopped taking the drug while traveling abroad.

The entire effort, as the staff assembled in the fall, was concentrated on locating yellow fever. It was known to occur among the Europeans, and indeed an outbreak was currently in progress in Lagos. There was some question whether Negroes got the disease and, if they did, whether it made them very sick. It was not only that jaundice is harder to detect in a black man, but what went on in the native compounds, with their mud-walled, windowless, thatch-roofed huts and narrow alleys, was a mystery. The Africans distrusted white medicine and harked to their witch doctors. They endeavored to hide their sick from "the white master" and buried their dead in the dirt floors of their dwellings. When this handy cemetery was full they abandoned the house and their dead as well.

The first large epidemic of yellow fever wholly among Negroes ever observed in West Africa occurred in the summer of 1926 in Asamankese, a town of 5,000 about fifty miles from Accra. Dr. William A. Young (1889-1928), director of the British Medical Research Institute in Accra, and Dr. Allen M. Walcott (1884-1962) of the I. H. D., from Lagos, investigated. At first the natives refused outside assistance. The village chief told Young and Walcott that the gods were scourging his people and must be propitiated; he kept the sick out of sight. A "juju man" from Togoland was hired to save the people of Asamankese, but his own assistant died and so did the chief's sister-in-law. The Yellow Fever Commission was then able to gain the villagers' confidence and make some examinations. The yellow-fever hunters discovered that Negroes could succumb to classic yellow fever, as well as have mild attacks that subsided in a day or two. The Asamankese epidemic totaled around 1,000 cases and perhaps 150 deaths.

Beeuwkes's laboratory people now began an intensive effort to uncover Noguchi's spirochete. This, in the minds of some officials, such as Simon Flexner, was the main object of the West African work—to settle whether *Leptospira icteroides* caused yellow fever or merely Weil's disease. They were sure that the leptospira caused one kind of yellow fever, but conceded that African might be different from American yellow fever.

By May 1927, several members of the staff, including Drs. Wilbur Sawyer, Henry R. Muller, and Johannes Bauer (1890-1961), had put blood from sixty-seven yellow-fever cases into guinea pigs, rabbits, white rats, white mice, African monkeys, pouched rats, puppies, kittens, and goats. They had nothing to show for their efforts but an occasional mild fever—no definite transmission of the disease.

When Beeuwkes returned to New York in 1927 he had only negative results to report—that plus the difficulty of keeping a good pathologist on the job. The man he had counted on, trained by Noguchi, was "scared, nervous, and unhappy," and had gone home. Another got a nasty falciparum malaria and also left. Beeuwkes wanted Noguchi to come to Africa; Flexner said Noguchi could go if, in another year, the Commission still had found nothing. This did not meet the immediate need. Beeuwkes said that he would like to get either Dr. Adrian Stokes (1887-1927), professor of pathology in Guy's Hospital Medical School, London, who had been a member of the Yellow Fever Commission to West Africa in 1920, or Dr. Wilhelm Schüffner, from Germany, who had repudiated Noguchi's *Leptospira icteroides*. Noguchi favored Stokes.

Walcott had proposed turning to human experiments, using Nigerian criminals, but this did not appeal to either Foundation or British colonial officials. Besides, many might be immune. Russell suggested that the Lagos laboratory use all the exotic animals it could get, on the supposition that they might lack the immunity African animals seemed to possess. Thus, on the way back to Africa, Beeuwkes not only stopped in London to persuade Stokes to spend six months in Lagos but also went to Hamburg, Germany, and ordered some Indian monkeys and Brazilian marmosets from Carl Hagenbeck, the animal dealer. Stokes was eager to make the expedition as long as the Foundation would buy him enough insurance, which it did.

Stokes and nine crown monkeys from India, imported from Hamburg, arrived in Accra by different boats but on the same day, May 24. He learned that a sizable yellow-fever epidemic was harassing the town of Larteh, thirty-two miles northeast of Accra. Stokes, bound for Lagos, another day's cruise to the east, decided to go ashore by the surf boat at Accra, with two chimpanzees he had purchased in Freetown, Sierra Leone.

In Accra to greet him were Bauer and, as soon as he got in from the bush, Dr. Alexander F. Mahaffy (1891-1962), a Canadian field investigator on the I. H. D. staff. On May 26, Stokes, Bauer, and Mahaffy drove to Larteh, where Mahaffy already had seen eleven persons with yellow fever. They drew blood from two Africans, a woman and a man, both of whom had fallen ill the day before. This blood they took back to Accra, mixed together, and inoculated into one chimpanzee, crown monkeys Nos. 10 and 11, twelve guinea pigs, and large numbers of culture tubes containing various media.

The guinea pigs and cultures turned out negative. The chimpanzee, previously recognized to be sick and emaciated, died ten days later of pneumonia and meningitis—no yellow fever.

But the two crown monkeys died ten and eleven days after inoculation following high fevers and, as the postmortem examination showed, an apparent yellow fever. Blood from Nos. 10 and 11 was now inoculated separately into Monkey 5 and Monkey 8 and more guinea pigs. Monkey 5 ran a high fever for four days, but recovered. Monkey 8 had an intermittent fever for four days and died of dysentery a month later.

These experiments were tantalizing but inconclusive. So were others that followed until the second chimpanzee and the remaining monkeys were used up. The chimpanzee survived its injection, unaffected. Stokes became fond of this chimp, a husky brute, and tried to make friends. One day Stokes came into the cage with an offering of food; the chimpanzee took it with one hand and with the other conked him over the head with a piece of chain that it had held behind its back.

At this point the first shipment of monkeys had been exhausted. Of six inoculated with yellow-fever blood, five had developed a fever and died while one showed no reaction. Of three inoculated with the blood of dead monkeys, two developed a fever and recovered, whereas one showed no reaction.

It appeared that at last a monkey somewhat susceptible to yellow fever had been found—that was good news—but the disease did not transmit too well. Efforts to infect African monkeys failed. No mosquito transmission experiments could be attempted. It was not possible to keep the Larteh yellow-fever strain alive.

In fact, the whole Larteh epidemic died out before a new shipment of monkeys arrived at the end of June. However, Mahaffy ran into a piece of luck. From the small town of Kpeve, Gold Coast, about 100 miles north of Accra, a European farmer and his wife had been brought in by ambulance with a diagnosis of typhoid fever, but it looked like yellow fever to Mahaffy. He rushed to Kpeve via Ho, Togoland, to pick up the district medical officer, and together they found six or eight natives convalescing from an illness. They saw one desperately ill woman, Felice, thirty, wife of a schoolteacher. She had a fever of 102°, a severe headache, and had been vomiting.

They also found a twenty-eight-year-old African named Asibi. He was sitting on a stool in a compound with his head in his hands. He said he had suddenly taken sick early that morning. He had a temperature of 103°. "We've got to get out of here," said the district medical officer, pointing to the aegypti mosquitoes flying around. Where there was yellow fever, there would be infected mosquitoes; a doctor poking around in a native village was taking chances. There was at least one tragic example on record. In 1921, Dr. Howard B. Cross (1888-1921), a Rockefeller Institute bacteriologist trained under Noguchi, on loan to the Foundation, had gone into a house at Tuxtepec, Mexico, to draw blood from a yellow-fever patient shortly before the latter died. Inasmuch as patients are infectious only in the first few days of their illness, in all probability it was a mosquito bite that caused young Cross's death from yellow fever. Cross was the first Rockefeller man to die from this occupational hazard. He had been preceded by two other medical scientists: Jesse Lazear, as we know, and Walter

Myers, a British doctor who died in Belem, Brazil, in 1901.

Mahaffy and his colleague made the rounds of more than 200 compounds, or families, but Felice and Asibi were the only suspected cases seen. The next morning, Mahaffy returned and got blood samples from both, though he thought he might be wasting his time. The woman was a little better, and Asibi was walking around, with only a little headache and low back pain.

Back in Accra that evening, June 30, Mahaffy turned the blood specimens over to Bauer. Hagenbeck had sent two kinds of animals in his second shipment, rhesus monkeys from India and Brazilian marmosets. Bauer, with Mahaffy helping, inoculated each specimen into a monkey, a marmoset, two guinea pigs, and a large number of culture tubes.

On July 2, Mahaffy returned to Kpeve to look for more cases. Felice had a normal temperature, but a definite jaundice and albumin and bile in her urine. Asibi was practically well and went back to work a couple of days later. Mahaffy came back to Accra a week later, feeling rather empty-handed. But the laboratory was in a state of excitement. Stokes was reviewing Bauer's experiments with him. Results with the Felice strain were mixed. Her blood had given a rhesus monkey a fever of 106°, but the animal recovered. It killed a marmoset, but an attempt to pass on the infection failed. The guinea pigs remained well.

The Asibi strain made history. The guinea pigs and marmoset were unaffected. But poor Rhesus 253-A, inoculated with Asibi's blood on June 30, developed fever on July 4 and the following morning was found breathing his last. Stokes immediately performed an autopsy. There was no jaundice, but the liver was characteristic of yellow fever—very pale and light-cream colored, with pinkish yellow centers in each section of the lobes. There were many hemorrhages, like tiny bruised spots, in the inner walls of the lungs and stomach, and a good deal of black blood in the stomach.

This was yellow fever. It wasn't Weil's disease, or Noguchi's disease, or any other disease they knew of. It did not infect guinea pigs or Noguchi's culture media. Noguchi had said that *Leptospira icteroides* would not infect monkeys, but this organism did.

The next step was to see if they could pass it on. Blood from Rhesus 253-A was injected into the abdomen of Rhesus 253-B, also injected with an emulsion of the first monkey's liver and kidney.

Now they would have to wait and see what happened.

The laboratory at Accra was unscreened, whereas they had special mosquito cages and rooms at Lagos. Bauer moved the second monkey to Lagos during its incubation period. Monkey 253-B developed a fever the day after it arrived, July 8, and, with the yellow fever circulating in its blood, was placed in a cage with seventy *Aëdes aegypti* female mosquitoes. Forty engorged themselves on the monkey's blood. Also, some of its blood was injected into Rhesus 209. No. 253-B ran a three-day fever and was found dead in its cage on the morning of July 11; No. 209 died the same time of day, on July 15.

Amazing. Yellow fever had been passed three times —not in stupid little guinea pigs which seemed to have been put on earth for two purposes, as foot warmers in the beds of South American mountaineers and as the proverbial, passive laboratory animal that bacteriologists and pathologists would have to vote Most Inoculable—but in monkeys, excitable little savages who resented their contribution to science every chattering, snapping millimeter of the way.

The important thing in the study of an infectious disease in a test animal is to keep it going—in a regular, predictable, unbroken chain.

The scientists set out to amass the evidence which they well knew, if it stood up, would restore Havana to its position as the cradle of the true faith in the etiology of yellow fever—and would make the great Noguchi look like a clown.

The laboratory division of labor was as follows: Bauer did all the mosquito and most of the monkey experiments. Dr. N. Paul Hudson, a bacteriologist, who came in August, did the postmortem examinations on monkeys that died during the day, and studied all disease findings. Stokes, who had an insomnia problem, offered to "post" all monkeys dying during the night.

Bauer could not get his African mosquitoes, held captive in test tubes, to bite monkeys, as Lazear had done twenty-seven years before in feeding his aegypti on human beings. So the feedings had to be carried on in the mosquito cages within a mosquito-proof room. How do you keep the monkey from breaking out of the mosquito cage or driving away the mosquitoes that are trying to bite him? Holding the animals in the cage with a leather-gloved hand was considered dangerous, as it was found that mosquitoes could bite through a stitch hole in the glove. The solution was to take gauze and bind the monkey on a padded board so he could "rest comfortably" with his head strapped to a cushion while the mosquitoes attacked him at choice points—face, lips, ears, and finger tips. The feeding went on for an hour. The monkey was then returned to its own cage.

Bauer found that as the infected mosquitoes grew older they became less inclined to feed in daylight and finally refused. It was possible to simulate night, however, by throwing a black cloth over the cage. Then they bit vigorously.

Bauer and his helpers handled their mosquitoes carefully. There were five to six screens between the insects and the outdoors. The mosquito room had a vestibule with two screened doors and each screened mosquito box had a cloth sleeve, through which the scientist worked with gloved hand. In the course of twenty-six mosquito-monkey transmission experiments, "No mosquito has escaped from the cage," the record stated.

With all this attention to details, the work went like a charm. Only twice in twenty-six instances beginning with a mosquito passage from Rhesus 253-B to No. 304 did infected mosquitoes fail to produce a fatal infection in a rhesus monkey. In one exception, the monkey had a fever but recovered; in the other, the monkey was unmoved by numerous mosquito bites.

Stokes, Warner, and Hudson found their yellow-fever agent would pass through a Berkefeld and other filters designed to hold back ordinary bacteria, so it could be classed as a filterable virus. In experiments beginning in early September, four out of five monkeys died of yellow fever following an injection of cell-free filtrate made from the blood of a monkey infected by mosquitoes. This confirmed Carroll's evidence of a filterable virus. They ruled out Noguchi's spirochete by showing that his immune serum did not protect their monkeys from fatal infection, whereas the immune serum that they made from the Larteh yellow-fever epidemic did.

The only virus skeptic remaining in Lagos was

Dr. Edward J. Scannell, who had extensive experience with yellow fever in Central and South America, and was still convinced that *Leptospira icteroides* caused yellow fever. Watching in the laboratory, he made good-natured remarks about their failure to find the *Leptospira* in humans or monkeys. These aspersions nettled Stokes.

Beeuwkes, of course, kept New York informed of this triumphant march of knowledge that, in the mid-century scientific terminology, would be called "a major breakthrough."

It was now time for Noguchi to go to Africa and defend himself. Joseph White, for one, went to the Rockefeller Institute and urged Noguchi to make the trip, adding:

"Are you prepared to face the possibility of being wrong?"

"Yes, I am prepared," said Noguchi.

His wife, Maizie, and friends tried to dissuade Noguchi from going. Noguchi was only fifty-one, but he had an enlarged heart and a mild diabetes. He was beginning to look old.

"But I am not afraid," he said. "I just want to finish this piece of work. I have been put into this world to do something and I want to finish it. I am enough of a fatalist to know that when my time comes I must go."

On September 16, 1927, Noguchi cabled he was coming to Africa. Beeuwkes got busy building a laboratory in Lagos for Noguchi's exclusive use.

Then, on September 19, Russell received a cablegram saying that Stokes was ill with yellow fever. The next day another message came: Stokes was dead. Russell and Sawyer, who was back from Africa, went to see Flexner and Noguchi. Noguchi said he planned to go to Africa; in a way he felt responsible for Stokes, having recommended him, he said.

First there were Lazear and Myers, then Cross—scientists who had given their lives in the fight against yellow fever. And now Stokes. . . .

Stoker was a kindly, tweedy sort of Englishman, just forty, charming with the ladies, not a big man, but an athletic type, a tennis player, with gray mustache and iron-gray hair. Hudson remembered that Stokes didn't take care of his fingernails.

It is usually impossible to say just when a virus enters the blood stream. Nevertheless, Stokes's colleagues knew that he was not infected by one of their mosquitoes; he was not working with them. But he was transmitting yellow fever, monkey to monkey, with the Asibi virus in their blood. He customarily worked without gloves. And he had a half-healed sore on one finger, from a monkey bite, as well as some cracks. The probability was that the virus found its way through his skin. A tremendous amount of virus circulates in the blood of a monkey during the first day of fever. Stokes was the first reported case of yellow-fever infection by this route.

Stokes became sick on September 15. He lived in the bungalow next to Beeuwkes. That day Beeuwkes was laid up with a carbuncle. After a good day's work, Stokes dressed Beeuwkes's leg and went to a dinner party. Feeling sick, he excused himself and went to his bungalow, where he vomited. He sent for Bauer. Both recognized the possibility of yellow fever.

"I feel awful," said Stokes. "Bauer, go get your squirt and get some blood to inoculate animals."

The next day, Stokes was moved to the hospital in Lagos. Stokes was not alarmed; in fact he was a little afraid that he might not have yellow fever. He told Beeuwkes that until now there had been no chance for a human experiment. He insisted that normal mosquitoes be allowed to bite him. Bauer applied 200 aegypti to his leg, and drew blood to inject into the monkeys. From Beeuwkes, Stokes exacted the promise of a complete autopsy if he died.

On September 17, Stokes felt better, but his eyes were sensitive to light. His heart and lungs were in good shape, but he had albumin and casts in his urine. He insisted that mosquitoes be allowed to bite him again.

On September 18, his mind was clear and he felt much better. He asked for books and talked of getting up and going into the laboratory. He also, as Hudson recently recalled, sent word that he would like to have Scannell and Hudson visit him in the hospital.

Stokes asked Scannell to make a diagnosis. Scannell examined Stokes in his low bed, in heavy silence. Scannell then put his stethoscope in his pocket and inspected the clinical chart and reports of laboratory tests.

The two men searched each other's eyes. "Well?" asked Stokes.

"I think you have it," said Scannell.

Stokes now asked him a series of questions, to each of which Scannell replied with a soft "Yes." He had watched them working in the laboratory. He knew what Stokes had been doing. He knew that he was not handling *Leptospira*. Then: "Have I been working with the virus?"

"That's what you fellows call it," replied Scannell.

This did not satisfy Stokes. "Are you ready now to agree, to admit that yellow fever is caused by a virus and not by *Leptospira?*"

Scannell hesitated, as though weighing his words, and then decided: "I believe you fellows are right. I don't have the explanation, but I think you have yellow fever and got infected in the laboratory with what you call a virus."

Perhaps there was gratification in Stokes's momentary silence, before he finally said, "Good-bye—Scannell, Hudson." He turned his face to the wall.

That evening his temperature was 101° and his pulse 70. He felt dull mentally, and during the night became delirious. On September 19, he was jaundiced, indicating liver damage. He fell into a coma during the day and died that night, at the end of his fourth day of illness.

"Hudson," said Bauer, a short time afterward, "someone must do an autopsy."

Hudson demurred; Stokes was a friend. "I don't want to," he said.

"Then I will do it," murmured Bauer.

Hudson saw tears in Bauer's eyes. Autopsies were Hudson's assignment and they both knew it. Hudson, out of professional pride, pulled himself together: "I will do it."

Hudson, performing the task about an hour after Stokes's death, found the pathology of a classic yellow fever.

Yellow fever was eventually passed via the mosquitoes and monkeys that received Stokes's blood. Also, Bauer and Hudson experimented with monkeys and proved that yellow fever could be transmitted by rubbing infected blood on the unbroken skin, provided the blood was from an early infection when the virus was multiplying.

Bauer, then thirty-seven years old, was a Swede who had trained in Germany and Russia as a bacteriologist. His associates recognized him as a meticulous investigator, disciplined and precise, although inclined to be a martinet. He had spent a year in Noguchi's laboratory in New York. In the original transmission of yellow-fever virus in monkeys, Bauer performed the critical experiments. Stokes was dead when it came time for Bauer and Hudson to write up the findings. As a memorial to their colleague, they decided the authorship should be "Stokes, Bauer, and Hudson," and this is the way their report was published.

It was the Asibi strain that killed Stokes. Descendants of this virus became the source of what has proved to be, in the opinion of many microbiologists, the best live-virus vaccine ever made. Mahaffy found it and Bauer preserved it in monkeys.

25

"I Don't Understand"

Hideyo Noguchi arrived in Accra on November 17, 1927, eager to work. He had made the usual three-and-a-half-week boat trip, via England. During this voyage, he slept almost endlessly, unusual for a man with the reputation for being a night owl, and he lost interest in his big black cigars. He still had not made up his mind whether he would work at Lagos with the others, who were now threatening to overturn nine years of his work, or alone at Accra. He did decide he would work not only with monkeys but chimpanzees and possibly a gorilla or two. The reported immunity of African primates apparently did not concern him. By radiogram he learned that he would have fifty rhesus monkeys from India to start with. But what about fresh blood specimens? Another radiogram came back that there was no new yellow fever along the West Coast. So he would have to use the Asibi and Stokes strains.

Beeuwkes and a companion from the Lagos laboratory came over to Sekondee, Gold Coast, to meet Noguchi and accompany him to his destination. Accra or Lagos? He finally made up his mind. It would be

Accra. He got off there in the surfboat. A delegation
of various officials and doctors in the Gold Coast capital
met him, and he said: "Gentlemen, I shall do my best.
The results—I cannot say—they are not with me."

Of course not. It surprised no one that he preferred
to work by himself. It was common gossip that Noguchi
could get results alone that no one else could. Noguchi
could stay with Dr. and Mrs. Mahaffy; their bungalow
had a small room with a separate entrance. Mr. Batchelder, a medical student who had been working in the
Lagos laboratory, would be his laboratory assistant.
Dr. William A. Young would turn his Medical Research
Institute laboratory over to Noguchi. Within a few
days, however, Noguchi saw the spacious bungalow of
another doctor and appealed to Young to find him one
like it. Young did so, and had it screened immediately.
Now Noguchi was able to live by himself with a staff
of native servants, including a man who had cooked
for the Prince of Wales.

Unquestionably, they treated Noguchi as a sacred
cow. Everybody—the Rockefeller men at Lagos who
were setting the yellow-fever world on fire, the British,
his laboratory staff of forty Africans—went flat out to
please this Japanese bacteriologist whom Flexner ranked
with Koch. Noguchi announced he would work nights,
to be less disturbed, and assigned Batchelder to take
care of the monkeys during the day. He refused to let
the young man in his laboratory. He thus successfully
isolated himself from all the Americans. Soon he was
talking about "those spies from Lagos."

At first, Noguchi did not ask for mosquitoes; their
use in the British laboratory seemed out of the question,
due to lack of screens (but later he screened off a corner of the room and obtained some). He wanted the virus

from Lagos, in preserved tissues and in monkeys, he wanted culture media for *Leptospira*, and he wanted normal monkeys—monkeys and more monkeys. He was in Accra almost six months and in that time used probably 1,200 monkeys at fifteen dollars each. This was many more than Stokes, Bauer, and Hudson had used.

Noguchi's laboratory problem was to show either that African yellow fever was caused by a *Leptospira* bacterium or that South American yellow fever was different from the African, which Bauer had transmitted through a bacteria-tight filter—via a "cell-free" virus. There was another possibility—that there were just yellow fever and infectious jaundice. In that case, Noguchi's work with yellow fever was simply a perfectly rounded blunder.

At Christmastime, Noguchi felt ill and was taken to the hospital. No one knew what was wrong. He considered it a mild case of yellow fever. It might have been Weil's disease. At any rate, Noguchi credited his icteroides vaccine, which he had received in New York, as having saved him from serious consequences. He was not too sick; he gave the nurse trouble when he behaved like a child, and then explained: "I am Noguchi." It was difficult to tell whether he was being arrogant or apologetic.

But now he claimed to have a Noguchi strain of "yellow fever" organism. On the fifth day of his illness he ordered a monkey injected with his blood. He claimed that the animal had black vomit for a whole week, January 2 to 9, a most peculiar finding, to the minds of the experts. Yellow fever from onset to death was usually over in a week or less. The monkey didn't die until January 17, and Noguchi autopsied it within the next thirty minutes. "The most typical yellow-fever liver I have ever seen in man or animals," said Noguchi. But the monkey had had no fever, jaundice, or albumin in its urine. It was a peculiar case.

Noguchi besieged Beeuwkes with requests for more monkeys, and for an animal house twice as big. The one he had was designed for fifty monkeys, and he had been packing in as many as four hundred. He said that errors were occurring because of overcrowding. This was not the only reason. In Lagos, the monkeys were kept in single cages and each had his number tattooed on him. Noguchi put two or three in a cage with their numbers on collars. Sometimes their collars got torn off. So which was which and who had what perhaps was decided in some instances a little like a game of ring toss. Noguchi liked guinea pigs much better.

During the late winter and spring he worked at a furious clip, and meanwhile dashed off cablegrams to New York. His cable bill ran as high as $1,800 a month and one message alone cost $250. He made important pronouncements, but sometimes merely soliloquized: "I am sitting on my bed looking at the wall . . . My work is so revolutionary that it is going to upset all our old ideas of yellow fever . . ."

He wrote his wife and personal friends long letters. They were his private audience, so to speak. He told them of his discovery of the organism of African yellow fever, a more deadly germ than the one he found in Guayaquil, where they had begun the adventure with him in 1918. They passed the news on to the New York *World*. The story was that he had made the discovery through his own illness. On April 21, Noguchi wrote Russell that he was demonstrating his new discoveries to Young.

Noguchi made plans to sail for home the third week

of May. On May 9, Beeuwkes, returning to Lagos from a conference in Dakar, arrived off shore at Accra, and Noguchi boarded the ship. Noguchi had not been to the Lagos laboratory and wanted to visit it before returning to New York. Noguchi went over his laboratory notes with Beeuwkes, who was astonished at the volume of work but found the data confusing. Noguchi himself, Beeuwkes said, was not certain where he stood. He had worked with several strains of yellow-fever virus in addition to his own, and his results were irregular (as they had been in Guayaquil). "You will think I am crazy when I tell you that I can boil the virus and still infect monkeys," Noguchi told Beeuwkes. It would be a hardy organism, indeed, that could survive a temperature of 212°F. if actually exposed to it. As an explanation, Noguchi claimed he was dealing with a spore-bearing bacillus. Except for Young, who said he was much impressed with Noguchi's work, the latter admitted only untrained helpers to his laboratory.

But now at this late date he was seeing the Lagos laboratory, which had no inhibitions against qualified visitors. As he went over the Lagos records, Noguchi expressed surprise that Stokes, Bauer, and Hudson had had such uniform results, so much in contrast with his own.

He had struck Beeuwkes as looking very tired, and while at the laboratory had felt chilly and indisposed. Noguchi asked Hudson to make a blood smear and look for malaria parasites. None was found. He asked Hudson not to mention his sickness to Beeuwkes. He wanted to get back to Accra. He had another chill during the overnight boat trip and was ill on arrival the morning of May 12. It was raining and the seas were running high.

The crew lowered him in a chair into the surfboat, and he made a dangerous landing.

The Mahaffys put him to bed at their house, Mahaffy strongly suspecting yellow fever even though Noguchi claimed to have had it and therefore would be immune. His temperature was 102.4°, pulse 88, and his urine heavy with albumin. Mahaffy took him to the hospital on May 13, where he vomited dark blood. Noguchi now knew he had yellow fever, and lay very still.

Mahaffy cabled Beeuwkes, to tell him of Noguchi's illness, and Beeuwkes and Walcott drove overland from Lagos to Accra, through Dahomey and Togoland, arriving on the sixteenth. By then Noguchi was much improved. His temperature had become subnormal on the fourteenth, but the doctors suspected this turn as the famous false remission of yellow fever. Still, Noguchi might be different—you could almost count on that.

Beeuwkes visited the laboratory with Young, who had so kindly turned it over to Noguchi. Many monkeys were dead. The rest they killed for safety. The two doctors locked up the laboratory.

For three more days, Noguchi's condition varied: "much improved," "rational, but no better," "quite well." He talked freely, and inquired about his laboratory. Then, on Saturday morning, the ninth day, he had a seizure, like an attack of epilepsy, and bit his tongue. Afterward, he was drowsy and weak.

Young visited him.

"I don't understand," murmured Noguchi.

Did he mean that he did not understand how Young, who had been in the laboratory observing Noguchi work, could be well? Or did he mean he did not understand how he himself could have yellow fever? Perhaps the latter.

That night Noguchi became worse. The next morning he was mentally confused and had toxic convulsions, due to kidney failure. He died at noon, Sunday, May 20, 1928.

Yellow fever customarily takes six to seven days to kill. Stokes went in four; Noguchi, in ten.

Two days after the autopsy—yellow fever, confirmed—Beeuwkes visited the Noguchi laboratory again. The windows were closed, but there were aegypti mosquitoes flying around inside, presumably from the mosquito room in the corner. In fact, one bit Beeuwkes (who, previous tests had shown, was immune). These mosquitoes could have been the source of Noguchi's infection, possibly, and also Young's later.

But Young might have been exposed when he took blood from Noguchi at the beginning of his sickness and inoculated it into a monkey, which died. Anyway, Beeuwkes had just arrived back in Lagos when he received a message from Mahaffy saying Young was down with yellow fever. Young died on May 30, only ten days after Noguchi.

Agramonte was the only yellow-fever expert not disposed to take the forthcoming bland eulogies of Noguchi in the press in silence. In August 1928, he spoke out in a letter to *Time*:

"Dr. Noguchi was one of the greatest bacteriologists of modern times . . . but his work in yellow fever from 1919 to the day of his decease was practically valueless and possibly harmful"—valueless because he was working with Weil's disease; harmful because his vaccine and serum gave a false sense of security.

Some bacteriologists, resentful of the insults to their intelligence imposed by the unquestioning acceptance of Noguchi's work by high authority, were prone to speculate that he committed suicide rather than return to New York as a failure. Whether or not Noguchi's death was a Japanese bacteriologist's hara-kiri cannot be certainly established. It did seem that death was the only way out of the mess into which his egocentrism had carried him. And it did seem that in winding up with yellow fever he impaled himself on his own ignorance or confusion. The infection, however, could have been accidental. Suicide is an intentional act, and in Noguchi's case would have required him to recognize the virus of yellow fever as an instrument for his self-destruction. He would first have to believe himself susceptible; as we have seen, Noguchi at Christmas-time believed that he had yellow fever; he also believed that his vaccine had been partially protective. He therefore must have believed himself immune to yellow fever —unless he later completely changed his mind on what he had had.

There was some feeling among the Lagos laboratory group that he had done so, not long before his death. Hudson recalled: "He told me that he accepted the virus etiology," although Noguchi added that it was some other source, on which he was working, that caused complications in yellow fever leading to death. It is conceivable that Noguchi was making some sort of heroic test on himself. But it was also generally observed that he was a "sloppy technician," whose experiments could not be repeated; that the more plausible theory is that, in infecting himself, he did not know what he was doing.

In any event, now the score against yellow fever read: Lazear, Myers, Cross, Stokes, Noguchi, and Young. . . .

26

Yellow Fever Loose in the Laboratory

Dr. Frederick F. Russell, an old laboratory man himself, knew he had a tiger by the tail. He had no desire to let go, but after the deaths of Stokes, Noguchi, and Young he was afraid that the trustees of the Rockefeller Foundation might consider the yellow-fever program too dangerous and drop it. Consequently, he made a sounding. Word came that it was all right to go ahead. Russell's next step was to establish a Yellow Fever Laboratory in New York City. He felt the need to control events, and thought a referee laboratory far from the tropics and close to headquarters might be the answer.

When Russell first proposed the establishment of an International Health Division laboratory to the trustees, Simon Flexner balked. Russell addressed himself to the scientific question. Like any traditional bacteriologist, he had some difficulty thinking about a yellow-fever virus that he could not see under a microscope or "plate out." What was the nature of this organism that was smaller than any living cell, heretofore accepted as the basic unit of life?

And, from the practical standpoint of control, was

African yellow fever the same as the Brazilian yellow fever, which had continued to plague Brazil's northeast coast and in 1928 was producing the first epidemic in Rio de Janeiro in twenty years?

Ideally, it might be difficult in either Brazil or Nigeria to prove likeness or unlikeness, to identify one disease, two diseases, or even three. In subtle ways, the environment could bias the findings in one place or another.

Why not allow the I.H.D. to set up a yellow-fever laboratory at the Rockefeller Institute, where the necessary comparative studies could be carried out? Flexner said he wanted no part of yellow fever in his institution. It was a bad actor in the laboratory. It had just killed Noguchi, who was like a son to him.

There was another argument that Russell did not dwell upon; it more or less spoke for itself. The Rockefeller yellow-fever program had a strong competitor. Dr. Andrew Watson Sellards (1884-1942) of Harvard was on his way to Dakar, Senegal, in late 1927 to test for yellow fever in chimpanzees and monkeys when, in London, he heard that Stokes and the others had transmitted the disease in rhesus monkeys. He got together with the Frenchmen, Constant Mathis and Jean Laigret, at the Institut Pasteur in Dakar, and from a Syrian patient they passed yellow fever through *Aëdes aegypti* mosquitoes into monkeys. In March 1928, Sellards took this French strain in frozen monkey liver to Paris, London, and Boston. He also brought back infected mosquitoes. Thus, Sellards and his young associate, Max Theiler, who went on to win the Nobel Prize in medicine and physiology in 1951, became the first to work with yellow fever in experimental animals in an American laboratory.

After all the Rockefeller Foundation had invested

in yellow-fever control (and all that Noguchi had wasted in both time and money), it would have been a downright shame to see somebody else take the lead!

Russell maneuvered. He went and took a look at an old brewery near the Rockefeller Institute; he thought he might turn it into a laboratory. Flexner was opposed to that, too. He now made a concession. The I.H.D. could have some space in the Institute, but must operate it under the most rigid conditions of isolation.

Russell appointed Wilbur A. Sawyer, then I.H.D. director of Public Health Laboratory Services, to head the Yellow Fever Laboratory, and Sawyer persuaded Drs. Wray D. M. Lloyd (1903-1936) and Stuart F. Kitchen (1902-1964) from the University of Western Ontario to join his staff. They understood the danger involved. Flexner assigned them two rooms in the Institute's animal house at the outset.

They started work on a Sunday, June 24, 1928. They allowed no visitors during the mosquito season from June until October, and the Institute personnel generally shunned them, occasionally talking to them through the screened door, the rare bold one taking hold of the doorknob through his white lab coat to step inside. For the first several months they did all their own chores, such as feeding monkeys and cleaning cages. Later, they got four helpers, attracted to the work because it was described as hazardous.

They collected the virus strains to be studied—the Asibi, brought over by Bauer in frozen and dried monkey blood; the French, sent to them by Sellards; and a Brazilian strain.

There were problems in keeping the virus alive during voyages of as much as a month. It was Sawyer who found it could be preserved at least 150 days in infected monkey blood that had been frozen and then dried in a vacuum and stored in sealed glass tubes. Eventually, he learned to keep the virus alive indefinitely.

In its first year of operation, the Yellow Fever Laboratory found, through cross-immunity tests, that all three viruses produced antibodies that gave protection to monkeys first receiving immune serum and then exposed to infection. So the viruses were much alike. In all probability, South American and African yellow fever were one and the same disease. Further tests showed Weil's (Noguchi's) disease to be something else entirely.

Sawyer now turned his attention to the possibility of producing a vaccine. It was sorely needed by the yellow-fever hunters themselves. By the beginning of 1929, there were reports of ten laboratory workers stricken by yellow fever in London and Berlin, all from contact with infectious monkey blood or tissue. All recovered.

Sawyer was the first to come down with yellow fever in the New York laboratory, in April 1929. Then forty-nine years old, he arrived at the laboratory one morning at eight o'clock feeling as though he had taken cold. By eleven o'clock he had to go home. His head, back, and legs ached and his temperature was 102°. He ran a fever for seven days, remained in bed fifteen days, and did not get back to the laboratory for five weeks. He did not have jaundice or black vomit, but suffered from a severe and prolonged loss of proteins in his urine. He became weak and thin, and was still ten pounds underweight when he returned to work. But he recovered.

At the Rockefeller laboratory in Bahia, Brazil, Dr. Paul A. Lewis (1879-1929), fifty, from the Rockefeller Institute, was not so fortunate. Lewis, a virus expert,

tended to share the conviction Flexner still clung
to—that *Leptospira* was at the bottom of yellow fever
and that it could be made to grow outside of animals.
Lewis went to Bahia to see if he could repeat Noguchi's
findings in new outbreaks there. He bled monkeys, autopsied them, and handled blood for cultures. He
had promised to cable Flexner once a week as to his
health. In three days, three cablegrams arrived in New
York. The first said Lewis was sick with influenza, the
second that he had yellow fever, and the third that he
was dead. He was stricken on June 26 and died June 30,
1929. As Sawyer remarked: "It was the last gasp of the
Leptospira question."

There would be one more death. Theodore B.
Hayne, an entomologist on his second tour with the
Rockefeller laboratory in Lagos, was probably bitten
by an infected mosquito. He died in July 1930, the
eighth scientist to give his life in the investigation of
yellow fever.

Laboratory infections with recoveries continued.
A clinical report published in 1931 counted thirty-two
cases of yellow fever in scientists and technicians beginning with Stokes in 1927 and ending in New York in
1931 with Wray Lloyd, who was out sick for fifty-one
days. Seven had yellow fever in the New York laboratory, including Paul Hudson, back from Africa, and
Stuart Kitchen, as well as three technicians. Meanwhile
Max Theiler had a mild bout with the French strain in
Boston. About the only Rockefeller laboratory man who
worked intensively with yellow fever over a long period
of time and did not get it was Johannes Bauer, also back
from Africa.

Obviously, yellow-fever laboratory workers needed
a vaccine more than other people.

27

First Successful Vaccine

The man who made the first effective yellow-fever vaccine possible was Max Theiler. Frederick Russell, reviewing yellow-fever research in 1932, ranked Theiler's taming of the virus by passage through mouse brains as the third of three great advances up to that time. The first was the Reed-Carroll discovery that yellow fever was caused by a cell-free filtrate carried from person to person by *Aëdes aegypti* mosquitoes; the second, the Stokes group's establishment of the rhesus monkey as a susceptible laboratory animal and through this the identification of the virus causing yellow fever.

That Theiler (pronounced "Tyler") became the vaccine man was the result of the vagaries that so often characterize great discoveries in biology. Theiler emerged and persisted as one of the classic free spirits of science, the right man at the right place at the right time; an intellectual giant (physically, he is only five-feet-two) and yet one who failed to touch the proper bases for achieving high academic and scientific rank and security. Theiler lacked a doctoral degree, fell out with his professor, and quit the Harvard faculty, an unthinkable combination of professional defects.

Born in Pretoria, South Africa, in 1899, the son of a distinguished veterinary bacteriologist from Switzerland, Theiler, a mediocre scholar, went to a London hospital medical school and took the British examination to become a licensed physician (1922) and then spent four months in the London School of Tropical Medicine. There he learned of an opening for a research assistant in the Harvard School of Tropical Medicine, a part of the Medical School and School of Public Health. He and his professor, who proved to be Watson Sellards, accepted each other sight unseen.

After Sellards brought back the French strain of yellow fever in frozen monkey liver, Theiler got to thinking. He was more of the opinion—then only beginning to emerge in the new science of virology—that a virus was some kind of entity quite different from bacteria and would never grow in a lifeless medium—that in fact it was a submicroscopic sort of half life that could only perpetuate itself within a living cell. To Sellards, of the old school, the new virology made little sense. He thought yellow fever was caused by a spirochete as yet undiscovered.

In any event, Theiler was right about one thing: the monkey, although susceptible, was not an ideal animal to work with. It cost a lot of money to buy and keep; it appeared generally unhappy with science, being hard to handle. Theiler wanted to get the virus going in an animal that was small and cheap. Guinea pigs had been tried and found wanting. He also noted that others had tried mice, using the usual routes of injections under the skin and in the belly without result. At Harvard, however, Howard B. Andervont had recently shown that *Herpes simplex* (the "cold sore" virus) could be passed through the brains of mice.

Why not try that?

While Sellards was on vacation in the summer of 1929, Theiler began work with miscellaneous laboratory mice. He used a half dozen a week, for, although mice cost only a few cents apiece, he did not have support money even for them. Scientists would hate to admit it these days, but here was a case where the researcher found virtue in poverty.

Surprising things happened when Theiler delicately injected a solution containing fine bits of infected monkey liver through the skulls of mice. His mice all died in a week. Examining them, he could find no sure signs of yellow fever—no liver damage, no jaundice, only occasional blood in the stomach. Their brain tissues were highly inflamed. They had an encephalitis and not classic yellow fever.

Theiler passed his virus on from mouse brain to mouse brain to mouse brain. He did it three times and got the same results. What began as yellow fever continued as encephalitis in the brains of mice. When he injected the virus intraperitoneally, that is, through the peritoneum into the abdominal cavity, he got nothing. These mice had healthy livers. They lived.

Sellards, returning, was enthusiastic and gave Theiler a monkey to test. Altogether, Theiler managed to scrape together three live and susceptible rhesus monkeys and injected them with his mouse-adapted French strain. With the third passage virus, the first inoculated monkey died of yellow fever. With a later passage, the second monkey had a fever and lived. Injected with a still later passage, the third monkey did not even have a fever.

This opened up an exciting possibility. In mice, a virus that was not supposed to kill mice did kill them when injected into the brain. And, as he passed it along, Theiler found that it killed them more quickly. It became more virulent.

On the other hand, the wild virus from Dakar was supposed to kill rhesus monkeys without fail. Now that it had been passed through mouse brains, however, it seemed to be losing its punch in monkeys. Theiler was fast coming to the conclusion that he had tamed this virus—that, in scientific terms, it had become "fixed for mice." Louis Pasteur (1822-1895) and Pierre Roux (1853-1933) had done much the same thing with the virus of dog rabies, by passing it through rabbit brains. Its virulence became greater in rabbits yet attenuated for dogs, so that it produced immunity but no disease.

Associates to whom Theiler spoke of his experiments listened skeptically, shrugged, and said: "You have only one good monkey there. How can you be sure it is yellow fever?" They meant that the result in only one of the three monkeys confirmed that the mice had yellow fever—the one that died. But it was the two surviving monkeys that looked good to Theiler; as he saw it, they had lived through a yellow-fever infection that was supposed to kill them. He still had to prove that what came out of his mouse brain was the yellow fever that he put in and not the ordinary encephalitis that it appeared to be.

One piece of evidence occurred accidentally, at about the time of the thirtieth mouse passage or around twenty-five weeks after the mouse-brain work began. Theiler came down with yellow fever. It was a mild case, but typical in other respects. He was in the hospital a week. There was no doubt, eventually, that it was yellow fever, for later tests showed Theiler solidly immune to the disease.

What Theiler needed, he saw, was some kind of test to show that his mice had yellow fever. As a matter of fact, Beeuwkes, Bauer, and Mahaffy earlier that year had developed a neutralization test in monkeys that illustrated his need very nicely. The blood serum of a person who had had yellow fever, either recently or a long time ago, would protect monkeys inoculated with the Asibi virus, a monkey killer. The usual way of doing it was to mix the serum to be tested with a virus solution and inject them. If the monkey died, the person was susceptible. If the monkey lived, the person had acquired immunity, meaning that infection at some time had produced antibodies in his blood. In other words, the serum neutralized the virus.

Theiler devised a similar neutralization test in mice. Sawyer supplied him blood samples from laboratory workers who had had yellow fever and were immune, and Theiler also used his own. In all trials, their serum protected the mice from encephalitis when the mouse-adapted French strain was injected with the serum into the brain. In contrast, serum from non-immune persons did not save the mice. So now let the critics talk. What he was working with in white mice *was* yellow fever.

In 1930, after more than a year's work, Theiler was ready to publish. Dr. Hans Zinsser encouraged him to do so, but Sellards did not approve. He told Theiler that he was committing scientific suicide if he published. Fortunately, Theiler was only thirty and still young and rebellious enough to take a chance. He did not have too much to lose; he had been at Harvard eight years and had only one promotion, to instructor. His two articles on his discoveries attracted the attention of Russell and

Sawyer, who came up to Boston to see Theiler and questioned him at length. After this consortium, his relationship with Sellards went downhill fast. Sellards did not like the Rockefeller Foundation. Zinsser told Theiler he was stymied and therefore ought to "get the hell out of Harvard." Theiler went down to New York and applied to Sawyer for a job. Sawyer, eager to move ahead, was happy to have Theiler join the team in the Yellow Fever Laboratory, now expanded far beyond the original two rooms.

Sawyer, Kitchen, and Lloyd now fell to work producing a vaccine. Their immediate objective was to put an end to the yellow-fever risk to laboratory workers. This first effective human vaccine against yellow fever was prepared in two parts: (1) a 10 percent suspension of mouse-brain tissue containing the attenuated French strain in fresh, sterile human serum, and (2) a human immune serum from persons who recently had yellow fever, to be used in simultaneous injections.

There were numerous sources of immune blood right there in the Yellow Fever Laboratory. Theiler himself furnished a good deal of it. Thus in some of Sawyer's new vaccine it was Theiler's virus and Theiler's antibodies that did the trick.

Bruce Wilson had just returned on leave from Brazil. Sawyer asked him if he would volunteer to go first, recognizing that Wilson had no laboratory-acquired immunity and was usually ready for anything. Wilson said he would be proud to do so. Sawyer arranged with the Rockefeller Institute Hospital to place Wilson in a screened room under close observation, with a day and a night nurse.

Wilson received the vaccine on May 13, 1931. Sawyer, Kitchen, and Lloyd injected the serum in two places in Wilson's abdomen and then injected the virus in a third place. This virus had traveled a long way since it was first drawn in a blood specimen from the Syrian in Dakar—through mosquitoes, through monkeys, through mice, and now back into a human being regarded by his colleagues as one of the greatest public health field directors who ever lived.

Would it behave?

It did.

There was some soreness at the sites of injection —some redness and swelling—but this disappeared within a day. The doctors watched Wilson's temperature, pulse, and urine for ten days. He didn't turn a hair. He amused himself, as Kitchen liked to recall, by teaching the night nurse how to play poker. Wilson lent her the money and then won it away from her.

Wilson wound up with a very nice immunity and a certificate saying he was the No. 1 man to receive this vaccine. As soon as Wilson was in the clear, Sawyer went ahead and vaccinated another fifteen laboratory workers and, in the next four years, ran the number of I.H.D. laboratory workers and field men receiving the vaccine up to eighty-five.

It was a great technical triumph for Sawyer. It was the end of accidental infections in the laboratory. He recognized and said the method could not be widely applied to susceptible populations because it was not practical to bleed enough immune persons to furnish all the serum needed.

But it was now possible to move ahead free of worry about what co-worker would be the next to go. It gave Sawyer a sense of confidence.

28

Jungle Yellow Fever:
Another Lesson

The yellow-fever experts, achieving the upper hand over laboratory infections, now got on with their "knowledge explosion." Still, it was only gradually that they understood there was not just urban but something called jungle yellow fever, a mysterious new beast that came, like Carl Sandburg's fog, on little cat feet and sat looking over the city, awaiting a chance to enter. To put jungle, or sylvan, yellow fever on the map another scientific mistake had to be corrected. This was the old assumption that yellow fever could only be transmitted by the house mosquito, *Aëdes aegypti*. Sure, the disease might spread from time to time into rural areas, but tropical seaports had to be the endemic centers, or seedbeds. Gorgas and Carter said this. Everybody believed it.

The Rockefeller Foundation had been fighting *Aëdes aegypti* mosquitoes in the coastal cities of the Nordeste (northeast Brazil) with some success following an outbreak in 1923. Unquestionably, this African mosquito was still widespread there. The region has a six-month dry season and the townspeople stored water from the rainy season in their houses, quite to the liking of this man-loving, pot-breeding mosquito. As urban yellow fever periodically dwindled and flared, first the Brazilian government and then the Foundation lost interest in mosquito control. There was a widespread outbreak in the Nordeste in 1926, as the Brazilian army chased rebel troops into the interior. After that, all was quiet again. Official hopes rose that yellow fever was completely gone from the Americas.

Yellow fever waited until May 1928 and then struck Rio de Janeiro with its first epidemic in twenty years. The epidemic continued through 1929, killing more than 400 and extending itself in scattered fashion along the coast and into the interior. This was urban yellow fever, as far as anybody knew, and it effectively kicked off a period of disillusionment.

Embarrassed in the eyes of its people, the Brazilian government openly blamed the Rockefeller Foundation for the reappearance of the disease. The International Health Division had introduced the Carter-Gorgas concept of yellow-fever eradication and Brazil found it a snare and delusion.

From then on, however, Brazil treated yellow fever as a first-priority national health problem. After the Vargas revolution in the fall of 1930, Dr. Fred L. Soper found himself with the opportunity to develop a position of strength such as few health officers have known. Dr. Belisario Penna, the new national director of health, asked him to take complete charge of yellow-fever control everywhere in Brazil except the Federal District of Rio (later there, too).

Soper became director of the Cooperative Yellow Fever Service of Brazil's National Health Department and the Rockefeller Foundation and thereupon began a twelve-year experience that was to see the almost complete extinction of urban, or aegypti-borne, yellow fever not only in Brazil but, ultimately, the whole Western Hemisphere. This effort constituted the centerpiece of what authoritative sources have described as "one of the principal triumphs of preventive medicine." Jungle yellow fever was another matter.

Soper had prepared himself for his new job by spending three months in the Nordeste finding out what was going on, because "I never had killed a mosquito in my life." It cost Soper, then thirty-seven, twenty-seven pounds of weight to get the facts. He followed Brazilian mosquito inspectors from house to house. They were operating under the key-center rule that when aegypti larvae were found in less than 5 percent of the houses yellow fever dies out.

He already knew there was a certain amount of fiction here. The year before, a yellow-fever case was found only 200 meters from the Yellow Fever Service Office in Recife at a time when the aegypti-breeding index was reported to be 0.8 percent. A spot survey of a hundred houses in ten different parts of the city gave an overall index of 26 percent! Something was rotten in the State of Pernambuco!

Recalled Soper:

"I made it a point to start the day's work when the *guarda* [inspector] did, to work with him . . . doing everything he did, including the preparation of the daily work sheet. If the *guarda* climbed up on a roof to inspect roof gutters, I also climbed the roof." Trying to touch his feet down on the top rung of a ladder under an overhanging eave was a sensation that became etched in Soper's memory. He began in Belem at the mouth of the Amazon and continued from city to city along the coast. It was hot and humid, and it struck him that each inspector was overzealous to educate him.

"There were days," Soper confessed, "while these twenty-seven pounds were melting away, when I was so tired and hot that, had I not been under the eye of the *guarda,* I might have been tempted to abandon the house visit, hie me to a coffeehouse or beer joint and calmly falsify the house visit record."

It would be necessary hereafter for the chief inspector to map and flag every stop made by this lowest man on the totem pole, who week in and week out might become increasingly indifferent to being where he should be. And so it was that "The *guarda* who failed to die in an explosion in the Nichteroy Arsenal because of absence from duty was discharged on reporting alive for duty the next day."

Soper became, as some associates said, "a hard man to work for," although he liked to think that they meant he was a hard man *not* to work for. He was called many things, including "dictator," but out of his desire to achieve the goal of his hero, Gorgas, and out of the intimate experience of hunting mosquitoes in the heat of the day, it seemed, came his mounting obsession with detail and his success in building a mosquito-fighting organization driven by obedience to detailed orders and by a fanatical desire to destroy the last mosquito.

It was not Soper's original intention to eradicate *Aëdes aegypti* mosquitoes. Like other yellow-fever fighters before him, he wished only to reduce their number to a point where they could not pass yellow fever in the human population.

The methods of attack that Soper and Bruce Wilson, his No. 1 field man, employed during the next few years were based on the Gorgas house-to-house hunt for mosquito larvae, with the addition of some important refinements. In sum, they employed an army of inspectors who regularly hunted aegypti larvae through a given city or town. When the larvae became hard to find, the presence of an adult mosquito in the house became the telltale. Hidden foci of infection were often plainly revealed when captures of adult mosquitoes were spotted on a map; this was the signal for a special squad to come in and clean up the neighborhood.

Any water container found with larvae in it was oiled—that is, a film of kerosene and fuel oil was poured on its surface, rendering the water unfit for use. This became a great inducement to keep water jars clean and free of larvae. This effrontery was first undertaken in the name of public health on a voluntary basis, then carried out under a dictatorial decree by Vargas, and finally by constitutional law, so most people sooner or later became convinced of the need to comply. What else was a poor householder to do? What a few did was grab a knife and stab the *guarda* or chase him out of the house with it.

In 1933, Soper and Wilson recorded a complete absence of aegypti mosquitoes from some of the principal cities in the Nordeste. Not only endemic urban yellow fever but the mosquito itself was gone, the first time this had happened since Gorgas began mosquito control in Havana more than thirty years before.

From the port cities, the Yellow Fever Service carried the attack on the mosquito inland to the small towns and rural areas of six states in the Nordeste, greatly reducing the number of aegypti mosquitoes but not entirely eradicating them in this six-state area, thought to be the last great endemic focus of urban yellow fever in the Americas. The last case of endemic, aegypti-transmitted yellow fever in the northeast region was reported in August 1934.

Once again the story of the "conquest of yellow fever" seemed to be swinging toward a grand climax. Unfortunately, yellow fever is a spoiler of triumphant exits. By now, Soper and his Yellow Fever Service were recognizing the presence of yellow fever *in the absence of* the aegypti mosquito! Yellow fever was showing itself to be a disease involving other mammals than man and other mosquitoes than aegypti. "Therefore," Soper asserted, "the dream of yellow-fever eradication had been, from the beginning, impossible."

Yellow fever in the absence of aegypti was first identified in the Vale do Chanaan (Valley of Canaan), in the small state of Espírito Santo, north of Rio de Janeiro. The well-populated, coffee-producing area, romanticized in Brazilian literature, is in Soper's words "a fairyland picture of steep green hillsides and narrow well-watered valleys with homes scattered at short distances along the streams."

In January 1932, Dr. Alvaro de Mello, the health officer in the state of Espírito Santo, reported that he suspected yellow fever at Santa Thereza. Dr. Allen Walcott of the I.H.D. visited the Municipio of Santa Thereza and found none. Walcott drove to the top of the pass to the valley beyond. No aegypti mosquitoes having been identified in the valley, he saw no point in going on.

The Yellow Fever Service had second thoughts about the decision when in March a Brazilian colleague called attention to a suspected death from yellow fever in the valley. Autopsy examination of the patient's liver confirmed the diagnosis. The American and Brazilian health officers collected information on eighty-three suspected cases with nine fatalities occurring during the previous four months. The investigation uncovered a triple epidemic of yellow fever, malaria, and typhoid, all at the same time. "Black typhus" was the catch-all diagnosis. The epidemic was on the wane when discovered.

The yellow-fever team combed the state of Espírito Santo, although "combing" may not be the best metaphor for sampling the blood of the people and identifying the mosquitoes that commonly bit them. Immunity tests showed a surprisingly scanty background of past yellow fever in the valley, quite unlike areas where the disease was heavily endemic.

Entomologists turned up various species of mosquitoes, none of them *Aëdes aegypti.* One good reason for the absence of this mosquito was the fact that most of the homes had mountain streams running by the door so there was no need to store water. What was interesting about the mosquitoes in the valley was that they dwelt *away from the house.* Furthermore, the cases of yellow fever were scattered.

Experiments attempting to transmit yellow fever with any of the Vale do Chanaan insects failed, so the vector was never established. But the intensity of investigation was such that it overpowered mental resistance to thinking about "Yellow Fever without *Aëdes aegypti,*" the title Soper and his colleagues put on their published report. It now seemed quite certain that some mosquito not closely associated with man served as the forest messenger of yellow fever.

Jungle yellow fever was progressively illuminated by two new techniques, the so-called mouse protection test and viscerotomy.

Up in New York, Sawyer had become interested

not only in the development of a vaccine but of "some simple immunity test" that would determine the whereabouts of yellow fever. Since the history of a person's serious infections is laid down in the specific antibodies in his blood, an immunity test could be used to map the distribution of yellow fever throughout the world, Sawyer wrote in 1931.

"The test would be especially valuable," he said, "where the disease is present but is seldom or never recognized, and also where there is confusion of yellow fever with other diseases."

Theiler's mouse protection test seemed to be the answer Sawyer was looking for, even though it required six or more mice per test. The white Swiss mouse is easy to raise, breed, and ship. But injection of virus and immune serum into the mouse brain posed technical problems, such as the standardization of dosage, that Sawyer wished to avoid, so he and Lloyd in 1931 modified the test for wholesale use. Their new intraperitoneal test worked this way: Using larger doses to overpower variations in the susceptibility of the mice, they injected a mixture of serum and virus into the belly of mice. Previously, this had not fazed mice, but they found the virus, if no antibodies were present, would localize in the brain if they injected a bit of starch solution there. Sawyer's test did the survey job in a worldwide survey that went on from 1931 to 1936. We shall come to the results.

Down in Brazil, Soper and Brazilian doctors had a different idea. Its application provides the most lurid chapter in the long fight against yellow fever.

From time to time, pathologists making autopsies had agreed and disagreed on just what microscopic changes yellow fever produces in the liver. The Rio de Janeiro yellow-fever outbreak of 1928-1929 provided

Brazilian doctors an opportunity to determine the validity of previous observations. Experience during this epidemic showed that, although differences of opinion might exist in some cases, the expert could diagnose yellow fever positively when a man died by opening him up and looking at a bit of his liver. This was of no help to the victim, of course, but it was important to epidemiologists. It told them where unreported yellow fever *had just been,* in contrast to the mouse protection test showing where the disease *had been at some time.*

The routine collection of liver specimens for the detection of endemic yellow fever began in the spring of 1930. The first autopsy revealed an unsuspected case of yellow fever.

Doctors were scarce, and the civil registrars were in charge of mortality records. The Yellow Fever Service instructed them in how to secure a liver specimen and offered cash payment for each specimen forwarded to the Health Department. Cemeteries needed a death certificate to permit burial, and the registrar was now required to clear all deaths with the Yellow Fever Service before issuing a certificate.

One great obstacle to the plan was the average Brazilian's revulsion for autopsies. The body of a loved one was sacred and to mutilate it was tantamount to blasphemy. Another obstacle was that some rural families buried their dead in the nearest suitable plot of ground without reporting them. Tracing the whereabouts of yellow fever by autopsy promised to be no easy job.

Nevertheless, Soper in June asked Dr. Elsmere R. Rickard to organize a "liver service" in the state of Pernambuco. Rickard was born in Weeping Willow,

Nebraska, and had a dapper look and a touch of genius about him.

If liver specimens had to be collected by laymen, in the absence of physicians, they ought to find a simpler way of snipping out a bit of liver than opening up the abdomen, Rickard told Soper. The latter agreed and remarked that they needed an instrument such as the buyers used to sample bags of coffee beans. These gentlemen slid a narrow, cone-like instrument through the loose burlap mesh, allowing a few beans to spill out without tearing the sack.

At Recife, Rickard devised a "viscerotome" and tried it out on beef liver and then in the local morgue. A metal trough with a sharpened nose and pointed blade that slid in grooves along the top of the trough, the viscerotome could be pushed through the abdominal wall into the liver, the sliding blade then retracted, then pushed farther in and finally closed again, so that a tiny block of liver would be punched out.

This gruesome piece of gadgetry became an instrument of triumph—and terror—finally being backed up, as it came into wider use, by a presidential decree, which said: "The practice of viscerotomy and routine autopsies is hereby established wherever desired by the (Yellow Fever) Service."

Beginning in the states of Pernambuco and Ceara, the livers of 28,468 recently deceased were collected and examined at the Bahia laboratory in three years. Seventy-five were found positive for yellow fever, fifty-four not having been recognized as such in the living person. Forty-four of these sporadic cases came from vast hinterlands in Pernambuco and Ceara, currently beset by drought, famine, and malaria.

So there were unknown sources of yellow fever far from the port cities, which were currently free of it. The viscerotome not only punctured livers but the key-center theory. It wasn't necessarily failure of anti-mosquito programs in the cities that kept yellow fever going year after year. There was a kind of "silent village," or rural, yellow fever that furnished some seedbeds. This was not jungle yellow fever. Aegypti mosquitoes were present.

Most of the fatal cases were among small children. The death of a child out in the country caused little comment. Authorities such as White, Carter, and Conner had received reports mostly of city cases. In other words, the key-center theory was built on the whereabouts of death records rather than of yellow fever.

Rickard noted the negative side: "In Ceara and other areas at least five viscerotomy agents were killed by the families of the deceased."

He had hoped that replacing the autopsy with the simple liver puncture would reduce opposition of relatives to "mutilation" of the dead, and it did work in that direction but did not quite eliminate the problem. Not quite.

The viscerotomist is simply a man, sometimes the registrar, appointed to do the job of collecting liver specimens, at so much per piece. The viscerotomy is usually performed at the cemetery while the corpse lies in the coffin fully clothed. Simply by opening the clothing at the waist it is possible to make the puncture without touching the body. An experienced viscerotomist can do the operation in thirty seconds or less.

This is well, because, while the government may authorize him to do this before the burial, he does not always have the consent of the family. The lack does not deter him, in view of the fee, but he often has to work fast and surreptitiously.

A viscerotomist in São Gonçalo, western Pernambuco, was said to carry a pistol in his right hand and a viscerotome in his left. During one yellow-fever outbreak, he got six liver specimens in this fashion.

The viscerotomist in Juazeiro was less fortunate. A family, finding it impossible to bury a daughter in Juazeiro without viscerotomy, took her body to the next town. Upon arrival in the second community, they found that the Juazeiro viscerotomist had informed the viscerotomist there of their coming. They permitted the second viscerotomist to perform the operation on their daughter's body at the cemetery. Following the funeral, the first viscerotomist was sipping beer in a cantina when the girl's three brothers walked in. They promptly closed in on him. He pulled out a large nickel-plated revolver and shot the first one. Unfortunately for him, the weapon jammed and he went down under the knives of the other two—stabbed to death.

The common belief seemed to be that the body must be kept intact for the second coming of Christ, when those who would be saved would rise from their graves. After the killing in Juazeiro, Padre Cicero, a much-revered, though unfrocked, priest straightened his flock out in behalf of his I.H.D. friends. He told people that God wanted their souls and hearts but did not care about the liver.

Wilson reported in his diary on "The Battle of the Viscerotome," detailing the troubles. When Sawyer received the report in New York, he cabled Soper to stop the viscerotomy program. It is not that easy, however, to reverse presidential decrees, and viscerotomy continues in some parts of South America today.

Viscerotomy combined with mouse protection tests to raise the curtain on the present and past whereabouts of jungle-centered yellow fever.

The worldwide survey, directed by Sawyer, by 1937 had shown yellow fever to be indigenous in only two areas of the world, Africa and South America. The mouse protection test revealed the disease to be far more prevalent in West Africa than anyone had imagined. All told, 25 percent of the people tested were immune.

Gorgas would have been dumfounded by the range of surprises in South America. For example, there apparently had been no yellow-fever epidemic in Manaus, capital of the state of Amazonas, since Oswaldo Cruz attacked aegypti there in 1912. The immunity survey confirmed this by showing no human adult in Manaus was immune. On the other hand, there were now plenty of aegypti. In contrast, there was a 50 percent immunity to yellow fever elsewhere in Amazonas, often *in the absence* of aegypti. Out there in the rural towns—many no more than clearings in the tropical rain forest—was an endemic lock with no key at all!

Aegypti mosquitoes were sometimes present, sometimes absent. Said Sawyer: "The immunity survey of South America shows that yellow fever continues endemic in vast areas of Brazil, Bolivia, Peru, Ecuador, Colombia, Paraguay, and Venezuela, long considered free of the disease." Eventually the known range of jungle yellow fever extended from northern Argentina to Mexico.

Henry Carter was writing his magnum opus on the urban epidemiology of yellow fever when he died in 1925. It was published posthumously, in 1931: *Yellow Fever: An Epidemiological and Historical Study of Its Place of Origin.* The book met a sad fate; it was yesterday's news and soon made no sense at all in the face of jungle yellow fever.

The information to refute the key-center theory and establish yellow fever as originally a jungle, rather than city, disease was right there almost under the noses of the yellow-fever fighters all the time. Time after time over the years, their attention had been called to the deaths of hundreds of monkeys in the jungle due to some mysterious epidemic. In 1914, Dr. Arthur Balfour (1873-1931) from Great Britain, witnessing such a monkey epidemic during an outbreak of human yellow fever in Trinidad, wrote an article in *Lancet*: "Wild Monkey as a Reservoir for the Virus of Yellow Fever." Yellow fever at the Muzo emerald mines in Colombia had been reported many times since 1907; forest mosquitoes had been suggested as carriers. Gorgas, investigating reports of cases at Muzo in 1916, dismissed yellow fever from consideration. Why? Because he could not find aegypti around the houses. Dr. Hugo Muench in the mid-1920's brought back reports of red howler monkey bands dying in Dutch Guiana, and Frederick Russell told him: "Don't be a fool." He said that aegypti mosquitoes don't bite monkeys, and monkeys don't get yellow fever.

It is true, of course, that *immune* monkeys do not get yellow fever. The West African and also Brazilian work established that many native monkeys have yellow-fever infection without showing it, whereas some species are highly susceptible. It was also found that yellow fever could be transmitted, at least experimentally, through a dozen different kinds of mosquitoes in Africa and South America.

If one assumed that these new facts turned on JUNGLE YELLOW FEVER in neon lights, however, he would have overlooked the formidable difference between the prospective and retrospective viewpoints. It took several years to weld together the evidence of susceptible jungle monkeys and susceptible jungle mosquitoes and get "jungle yellow fever," a term that Soper first used in 1935.

It was apparent that yellow-fever virus was present in the forests. But what was its animal host? What insect carried it? How did it move out of the jungle and into people?

It was Allen W. Burke who first put the finger of suspicion on a small metallic blue mosquito named *Haemagogus spegazzinii*. This and two other forest species were the only ones present during a 1935 outbreak of jungle yellow fever on the plateau of Matto Grosso. People working in the forests and nearby fields complained that the little blue one was a vicious biter, the others less so. Paulo Antunes and Loring Whitman found this *Haemagogus* difficult to work with in the laboratory but did manage to infect it with the virus and so transmit yellow fever to monkeys in 1937.

Then, in 1938, Raymond Shannon, Whitman, and Mario Franca made a good case against both the spegazzinii and another *Aëdes* mosquito known as leucocelaenus. In a period of six years, there had been more than twenty small outbreaks of jungle yellow fever in Brazil, Colombia, Peru, Paraguay, and Bolivia. In most of these instances, people—mainly men—got yellow fever while going out in the forest or jungle. During a 1938 outbreak in the state of Rio de Janeiro, the Shannon group collected 24,304 live mosquitoes from the jungle near places where there had been human infections. These mosquitoes were identified and set to biting non-immune monkeys. Among thirty-one species of mosquitoes caught, *Haemagogus* and *Aëdes leucocelaenus* were among the most prevalent. Each of these species, biting in groups, infected a monkey with yellow fever. It was only two monkeys, but it was an important finding that, as the three investigators said, "Incriminates two species of forest-inhabiting mosquitoes as natural vectors of yellow fever." Shannon knew what he had: the first evidence that other specific mosquitoes besides *Aëdes aegypti* carried yellow-fever virus in their wild state.

Meanwhile much the same story was being recorded in the I.H.D. laboratories at Bogotá and Villavicencio, Colombia. Dr. John C. Bugher of the I.H.D. and Dr. Jorge Boshell Manrique, a Colombian, became the chief investigators of jungle yellow fever in Colombia. They had a mobile field laboratory, organized to take off promptly on any interesting leads. Their objective was to wring out the mystery of jungle yellow fever. During the first two years, about the only new observations they made were that the marsupials—most commonly the opossum—and also some other animals—the peccary and the armadillo, for instance—are variously susceptible to yellow fever in the laboratory. After 1940, so much happened and made such dramatic news that Colombia stole the show from Brazil.

The big difficulty that Bugher and Boshell had to solve gave direction to their findings. Mosquitoes of all kinds were scarce, due to a continuing drought, and it was hard to get a line on *Haemagogus spegazzinii* and the other forest mosquitoes under suspicion. Boshell was personally familiar with the behavior of jungle yellow fever. The persons who got it were usually woodcutters, farmers clearing land, or road builders. Once a child developed the disease after carrying lunch to his father at work in the woods. The woodsmen said one thing over and over. If they merely walked through the forest, they seldom saw a mosquito, but while they were chopping trees they would be attacked by large numbers. These were the shiny blue ones.

Then, while investigating two cases of yellow fever reported from the headwaters of the Rio Ocoa, Boshell in late 1940 saw through the whole mystery. His group, coming down the mountain, stopped to watch some men felling a tree. There were no mosquitoes in sight. But when the tree came crashing to the ground, tearing limbs from other trees as it dropped, Boshell saw mosquitoes swarm around the woodcutters, biting viciously.

So then . . . *Haemagogus* dwells in the treetops.

For the next several years, this fact was the basis for intensive investigation. The broad outline of the new discovery emerged. This mosquito lived in the forest canopy and fed on the monkeys that also lived in treetops. Its favorite in Colombia was the saimiri, or squirrel monkey.

Haemagogus is a daylight feeder, a sun lover, and likes to take its meal around noon while the monkeys are having a siesta.

It took a great deal of doing to climb the trees, capture the mosquitoes, and trap monkeys, but soon Bugher and Boshell had a monkey-mosquito-monkey cycle of yellow fever going in the laboratory, a parallel of what was happening high above the jungle floor. It is the mosquito, more likely, that keeps the virus going, inasmuch as the *Haemagogus* infected with the virus may live in the treetops during a dry season and thus carry yellow-fever virus over from one rainy season to the next. To start an epidemic, an infected mosquito must meet a non-immune monkey or man. The mosquito does not necessarily wait for a man to chop down a tree. *Haema-*

gogus descends to ground level at the edge of the forest and bites anybody it finds there. And it can furnish the spark for urban yellow fever if the monkey or man it infects is then bitten by *Aëdes aegypti* living around a house.

Aëdes aegypti remained the key to eradication of urban yellow fever. As early as 1934, Soper began talking about the total elimination of this mosquito from Brazil. Yellow-fever experts from Rio to New York laughed at him. They declined to be Soperized, and some questioned his sanity.

Soper agreed that jungle yellow fever constitutes a permanent source of virus from which cities and towns could be reinfected. But, he hastened to add, they could not be reinfected on any continuing basis if they contained no aegypti mosquitoes. Cases of jungle yellow fever might come to town, but forest mosquitoes that carried the virus would not. Far from throwing up his hands or quitting the field, Soper merely shifted his target from yellow-fever eradication to *Aëdes aegypti* eradication.

The preponderance of opinion was that aegypti eradication would not work. One argument against it was the "sanctity of species," meaning the seeming determination of all living creatures to overcome obstacles and perpetuate themselves. Another was that there would be an irreducible minimum, no matter how good the control measures. The law of diminishing returns from long-continued effort was cited. Practical minds offered another argument that was difficult to counter. This was the danger of reinfestation. Even if you drove this mosquito out of Brazil, an enormous area, the aegypti mosquitoes in Paraguay or Argentina were not apt to respect the national boundary.

In 1938, Soper raised his sights and proposed to the Rockefeller Foundation a program for the eradication of *Aëdes aegypti* throughout South America. He offered to use some of his highly trained Brazilian doctors to help organize and operate anti-mosquito programs in other countries. Sawyer, who was by this time I.H.D. director, turned him down.

In 1940, the International Health Division, with American involvement in a European war in prospect, withdrew from the anti-aegypti program in Brazil. It was another setback for Soper, who two years later was transferred to North Africa and soon found himself fighting typhus, malaria, and the high brass. At the time the Foundation "phased out," the aegypti mosquito was nowhere to be found in the national capital of Rio de Janeiro or in six of Brazil's twenty states. Brazil continued the Yellow Fever Service during World War II. By 1947 the Amazon Valley of Brazil and all of the nation south of Bahia was cleared of aegypti, and the known infested areas in the Nordeste were shrinking. But Brazil was having reinfestation problems along its borders.

In 1947, Soper was able to get down to business again.

He became director of the Pan American Health Organization and in 1949 regional director of the World Health Organization. Brazil, noting that it had ten frontiers with neighboring countries, proposed a program to eradicate *Aëdes aegypti* from all the Americas, including the United States, where this mosquito was still to be found in some southern states. Soper recommended that P.A.H.O. approve of this proposal, and it did so. The advent of house spraying with DDT in fighting malaria mosquitoes was a great boost to the war on aegypti.

Progress in continental eradication was slow but gathered momentum. From 1947 to 1959, when Soper retired, there were only three cases of aegypti-transmitted yellow fever reported for the entire continent. The United States was slowest in joining in, since it had neither urban nor jungle yellow fever, but finally did so, in 1963, out of a spirit of international cooperation. Today, Brazil and all of South America are largely—not entirely—free of the "unpleasant Egyptian" except parts of Venezuela, French Guiana and Guyana (formerly British Guiana), and Surinam (Dutch Guiana). All of Central America and Mexico have practically eradicated the mosquito. Some West Indian islands and the United States remain on the black list.

Jungle yellow fever remains a constant threat. An epidemic wave of the disease, carried by forest mosquitoes and monkeys, moved north from Colombia through the Panama Canal Zone all the way to the southern part of Mexico between 1948 and 1958, here and there spilling over into the human population. Panama had not seen a case of yellow fever from 1920 to 1947. In 1948 and 1949, eight persons died of it.

In 1962, jungle yellow fever went on another prowl in Brazil, moving from the Amazon Basin into the Rio de la Plata Valley and spreading southward, far from the tropical rain forest. It produced sporadic human cases in 1966 in three states of southern Brazil and two states of Argentina.

The only South American countries considered safe from jungle yellow fever are Uruguay and Chile, which lack tropical or subtropical forests and monkeys.

"Voices," remarked Paulo Antunes, "have been heard in recent years saying that Fred Soper is obsessed with the idea of *Aëdes aegypti* eradication and that it is his sole subject of conversation. What a magnificent obsession! . . . Is not the virus of yellow fever still present in large areas of the jungle?"

Against jungle yellow fever itself there was only one hope—a good vaccine. Wilbur Sawyer was working on that.

29

A Good Vaccine

But how do you make a good yellow-fever vaccine?

Sawyer, Lloyd, Theiler, and their beautiful and competent senior technician, Miss Nelda I. Ricci, soon joined by the amiable Dr. Hugh H. Smith, had two models for virus vaccine.

Dr. Edward Jenner's cowpox virus as protection against smallpox was the better. The cowpox and human smallpox viruses probably stem from a common ancestor and are closely enough related to produce a cross-immunity, but, as diseases, behave quite differently. Cowpox occurs as a few small skin ulcers in cattle and human beings, whereas smallpox is a serious, spreading, and often fatal ulceration in man and some monkeys. The live cowpox virus, conferring an immunity that lasts most people three or more years, was at the time the only simple, safe vaccine that worked against a virus disease.

The Pasteur prophylactic treatment for the bite of a rabid animal, the second model, was not simple or wholly safe in its original form. The rabies vaccine consisted of first an attenuated and later killed virus in rabbit brain, given in daily doses of graded potency over a fourteen-day period. In a few human cases it produced an encephalitis or paralysis, more rarely death. But Pasteur had introduced this method of gentling a virus down: By passing the wild virus of dog rabies, a 100 percent killer, through the brain of one rabbit after another, he had "fixed" or attenuated it. The virus would no longer kill a dog, if infected under the skin, though it was still a killer if injected into his nervous system.

Most of the early virologists had played with the vaccinia virus—the laboratory name for the much-manipulated cowpox organism. Following the discovery of methods of growing living tissues in cultures, various scientists induced this virus to multiply under glass. After a start with fowlpox in 1931 Ernest W. Goodpasture (1886-1960) and his staff at Vanderbilt grew vaccinia virus in chick embryos—that is, in hatching eggs. These feats constituted technical triumphs over all manner of troublesome details.

It was perfectly clear to Sawyer and his talented virologists in the International Health Division Laboratories at the Rockefeller Institute that they had to do these same things with the yellow-fever virus. Virologists had gradually come to realize that these ultramicroscopic nucleoprotein particles called viruses would not, like bacteria, reproduce in a lifeless medium. When frozen or dried, viruses may survive as dormant seed, but they have to borrow some life to have any of their own, multiplying only within living cells.

The fundamental problem in taming the wild yellow-fever virus for use in a vaccine is its tendency to destroy the liver. It was a great breakthrough to get the virus out of human beings and mosquitoes into monkeys, yet as far as making a vaccine for millions of people was concerned, the infected monkey liver offered a draw-

back. The live virus, in its natural state, had this dangerous addiction to liver called viscerotropism. If the virus
was killed, as first attempted, people might require large
and repeated doses. This might introduce too much foreign protein, and lead to allergic reactions. This hazard
might be substantially overcome through filtration or
centrifuging but at some sacrifice of potency. The virus
does require the presence of some protein to survive at
all.

A filtered solution of the "Theiler virus"—the
mouse-adapted French strain—presented hardly any
hazard as far as liver damage went; on the other hand,
being couched in the brain cells of a mouse, it had a
heightened neurotropism. Injected in the abdomen or
under the skin, it only occasionally found its way to the
brain, but even an occasional case of crippling or lethal
encephalitis would be enough to discredit the vaccine
for human consumption.

The unwritten law in vaccine-making is that you
must not create an actual danger to head off a potential
one. In public health statistics, it becomes a matter of
weighing a tiny number who would be harmed by the
vaccine against a large number who would be harmed
by the disease if all were not vaccinated. Nevertheless,
when it comes down to the unlucky individual, it is easy
to see which way he would jump if given the choice of
possibly dying from a disease in the future or from a vaccine that he is about to have now. Why take a risk? The
burden is on the vaccine-maker to find a vaccine that
presents practically no risk at all.

The search began at the I.H.D. laboratory, on the
East River at 66th Street and York Avenue, with an attempt to grow the French mouse-adapted virus in tissue
cultures. Theiler assisted Dr. Eugen Haagen, a bac-

teriologist from Germany, in these experiments. They were the first to succeed in propagating yellow-fever virus in a culture of living cells, getting their best results with chick-embryo cultures. Haagen published the original paper in German, in 1932.

How could they tell that the virus actually multiplied and was not simply passed along from culture to culture? The standard method—in fact, the only method then, was through titration (from the French *titre*, or "standard"). A given virus solution will continue to infect test animals when diluted with a saline-and-serum solution up to a certain pre-established point. If it infects well beyond that point, then the virus must have multiplied meanwhile. By the twentieth subculture, they had diluted the original virus about five million billion times and it remained as infectious as before.

Happily, Haagen, who kept a picture of Hitler on his desk and engaged in Nazi Bund activities, returned to Germany after the Führer came to power and disappears from our story.

In 1934, Sawyer heard alarming news from the Institut Pasteur in Dakar. Sellards and Laigret in 1932 had experimented with a vaccine using Theiler's mouse strain, but they had some severe reactions in human beings and dropped it. Now Laigret had gone down to Dakar from the Pasteur Institute in Tunis with a virus —"attenuated," he said, by exposure to room temperature for one, two, and four days. It was given in three injections of increasing virulence at intervals of twenty days. This, in principle, was the way Pasteur had administered his rabbit rabies virus. Laigret did not seem to be getting any brain inflammation. As a matter of fact, he vaccinated nearly 6,000 Africans in this manner in 1934 and 1935.

Sawyer had not been so daring with his Theiler-virus vaccine for laboratory workers. He permitted its use only in combination with a human immune serum. Most monkeys receiving mouse-brain virus injections under the skin took it like lambs, but an occasional one developed a fatal encephalitis. The same thing could happen to human beings. The immune serum acted as a kind of buffer.

Theiler, never too vocal and not inclined to take strong stands, was so opposed to the use of his virus in the Laigret manner that he wrote an article on the "Danger of Vaccinating with Neurotropic Yellow Fever Virus Alone," and published it in Paris. He and Sawyer were skeptical that exposure of the virus to a temperature of around 68° for varying periods would reduce its virulence; the indication was that it simply died off.

Dr. G. Marshall Findlay (1893-1952) of the Well-come Bureau of Scientific Research in London, also engaged in yellow-fever vaccine development, heartily agreed with Sawyer and Theiler. From then on, the British and Americans looked askance at their French competitors.

Meanwhile, the French in Dakar became dissatisfied with their three-injection method, rather cumbersome to carry out in an uneducated, native population, and reduced it to one shot. They vaccinated 20,000 West Africans with one method or the other between 1934 and 1939. The records did not seem to show any particular trouble, but then it's hard to do follow-up studies on primitive people. According to hearsay, some had fever, headaches and jaundice; there were unconfirmed stories of deaths.

In any event, the news from Dakar stimulated the

I.H.D. to seek a better vaccine. By this time, Lloyd and Theiler were thoroughly bored with the French neurotropic strain. It was an uncooperative virus.

They decided to get away from the mouse virus and start all over again with some mild strains maintained in monkeys. For comparison purposes, they used the wild Asibi virus, itself a dangerous customer guaranteed to kill 95 of 100 rhesus monkeys four to seven days after injection under their skins. It was both viscerotropic and neurotropic, customarily attacking the liver but, in some instances, also the brain.

For three years, 1934-1937, the laboratory was like a factory engaged in the production of living cultures of tissues and virus. Hundreds and thousands of culture flasks were set up. They were subcultured every third to fifth day in order to stay ahead of bacterial contamination (nowadays, antibiotics are used to keep the bacteria down). Every conceivable kind of animal tissue was tried. If someone thought of the testicle of a mouse, in went some testicle of a mouse.

"There was no logic here," Theiler recalled. "We set up a machine and let it run. We established a system of culturing and subculturing the virus in various tissues, and had good technicians. They were the thing."

In other words, Miss Ricci and her helpers were the handmaidens of these virus-and-tissue fertility rites. The scientists simply spot-checked from time to time by injecting samples into mice and monkeys.

At first, the Asibi virus would not grow in any tissue cultures at all. After several attempts, however, they got it going in minced mouse embryo. Then, after eighteen subcultures in mouse embryo, they branched it off into minced whole chick embryo, where it now grew well. After fifty-eight passages in this fashion, they started a new line with brain and spinal cord removed. There was about a year's work right here.

All the culture flasks beginning with mouse embryo were labeled "17," this being the laboratory's seventeenth series of tissue culture experiments. A letter was added to the number to designate the tissue being used. The virologists had their first piece of luck early in 1935. After ninety-two passages in 17E, the virus still in mouse embryo became so attenuated in viscerotropism that monkeys survived when 17E virus was injected into their abdomens. It also became a little less neurotropic than the mouse-adapted French virus, but not enough so that it could be safely used for a human vaccine without immune serum. This, in effect, was the second vaccine developed by the I.H.D. laboratory.

Lloyd, an intense, clear-eyed, heavy-jowled young man of thirty-one with a barrel chest and short legs, was a demon for work. He was completely dedicated, never stuffy, loved beer. Before going to Brazil to test 17E, Lloyd wrote up all the Asibi experiments, signed the report "Lloyd, Theiler, and Ricci," and sent it to Sawyer for approval. Sawyer was delighted, but asked that Miss Ricci's name be dropped. He felt that scientific authorship should not include technicians. "In that case, I won't publish it," said Lloyd and chucked the manuscript in a desk drawer. It remained there for several months until Sawyer relented.

The best analogy for events in the I.H.D. New York headquarters and laboratory in 1935 was to be found in the ultra-centrifuge that Johannes Bauer and Edward G. Pickels were building in the lab for the study of virus composition: things were spinning. The Bauer-

Pickels techniques, not only in centrifuging but in freezing and drying virus mixtures, would play an important role in production of a vaccine.

Frederick Russell reached the retirement age of sixty-five and Sawyer succeeded him as I.H.D. director in September. Bauer took charge of the laboratory. Hugh Smith came in to follow Lloyd, who had married a beautiful Uruguayan girl in 1934, and now went to Rio de Janeiro. Smith, son of a South Carolina general practitioner, was a Johns Hopkins graduate, then thirty-three-years old. He fitted into the team well.

Theiler and Smith carried on the 17 line of virus-and-chick cultures. They had been divided in three directions. Asibi with: (1) whole chick embryo, 17D (WC); (2) chick embryo brain, 17D (CEB); and (3) chick embryo with brain and spinal cord cut away before mincing, 17D.

As Theiler said, "We let it run." So it went on culture to subculture, every few days, never more than a week. Contaminated cultures were thrown out. Here and there a mouse or monkey was tested. Years could go by in such dull routine.

Then, in April 1936, Smith looked at the results of a routine spot check. He noticed something and called it to Theiler's attention. The 176th passage of the 17D strain did not kill all the mice when it was injected into their brains. Some got a paralysis in their hind legs, but survived. When the virus was injected into the brains of two monkeys, they developed a mild encephalitis but survived. Monkeys receiving the 17D virus in the belly developed no sign of fever or illness. All showed beautiful antibodies when challenged with the wild Asibi virus, however. They did not turn a hair.

"This was the much-hoped-for change," Theiler wrote later.

At the time, however, he did little more than look up the record of the last monkey tests. He found that injections in the brain from the 89th subculture had killed three out of three monkeys. That was in January, 1935, about fifteen months and eighty-seven cultures before. It was obvious that it would take a lot of digging to find at what point the virus had become gentle. To carry the investigation forward from there to human trials represented a whole new program. It was wholly in character with Theiler as a free spirit that he did not drop everything to explore this new lead.

"From this," Theiler remarked of the change between the 89th and 176th passage, "it is quite apparent that we had the desired mutant in our hands for quite a long time, although we were not aware of it. The fact of the matter is that we were more interested in other things at the time."

In October 1936, Theiler and Smith found the opportunity to retrace the tissue culture steps as far as they could. Tragically, Lloyd had died in Rio in June. He fatally injured himself in a fall through his apartment window. There were two explanations: one that he was walking in his sleep, the other that he was hanging drapes in preparation for the arrival the next day of Mrs. Lloyd's parents from Montevideo. He did not live to know or share in the fame of 17D.

The laboratory technicians in the course of propagating various lines of virus at irregular intervals dried samples of the cultures and stored them. As mentioned, No. 89 of 17D had been lethal for monkeys. The next one saved had been No. 114. Testing this in brain injections, Theiler and Smith found that four out of four monkeys lived. The virus did not bother their livers at all. Further testing showed that whereas No. 89 was both viscerotropic and neurotropic, No. 114 had lost these qualities.

Thus, somewhere in the course of twenty-five passages between these two points, a spontaneous mutation had occurred. Evolution had taken place—so it appeared—in a bare-looking laboratory overlooking the East River. No one was looking. Apparently the change had occurred around a year before it was discovered. If this was the case, then it may have occurred in the late winter or spring of 1935.

It is most undramatic, but it is about as close as we can pinpoint this next great blow for freedom from yellow fever. It would seem that, in her greatest moments, nature eludes her stage manager. It is even difficult to name the stage manager; by the time the attenuation was discovered, Sawyer and Lloyd had left the laboratory. But Theiler and Smith were there. In November 1936, they tried the virus on themselves and on Dr. Thomas Francis, a newcomer to the I.H.D. and interested in influenza. All were already immune but tests before and after inoculation showed a big jump in their antibody titer, meaning the virus had a booster effect.

They had no other reaction; Theiler and Smith now went ahead and gave the 17D vaccine to Drs. Andrew J. Warren and Hugo Muench and then six other non-immune volunteers and gave it without the protection of immune serum. The main complaints were slight fever, headache, and backache, but nothing that prevented them from going about their work. All became immune to yellow fever.

Theiler and Smith now wrote two reports, on the virus culture and on the human tests, both published in the *Journal of Experimental Medicine*, June 1, 1937.

The only way they could explain the favorable changes in the virus was in the kinds of tissue cultures used. In mouse embryo, 17E had lost its viscerotropism. When this line was continued as 17D chick embryo without the presence of central nerve tissue the virus lost most of its neurotropism.

They were confident that these manipulations were the cause of the mutations. They later found themselves to be in error. When Theiler repeated the experiments with the brainless, spineless chick embryo, he was unable, after more than 200 subcultures, to show any reduction of neurotropism. What happened in the one 17D mutation? "There is no explanation," he said.

The practical importance of this gentle, new virus was not only its apparent safety, but the fact that, as mentioned, it could be administered without the addition of an immune serum. It did appear necessary to add about 10 percent of normal, non-immune human blood serum—plasma—to the solution drawn off from the tissue culture in order to keep the virus alive. In Bauer's experience, the yellow-fever virus died off within the day without this addition of blood proteins. This seemed to present no problem. Ordinary human blood is plentiful. They used it in the tissue culture too, instead of monkey blood.

With Smith, John E. Elmendorf, Jr. (1893-1960), another member of the laboratory, immediately made the first move to get 17D ready for mass production. Under the Goodpasture technique of cutting little windows in hatching hens' eggs, they found they could easily inject the virus into an egg. The window was closed, the egg incubated, and the virus flourished. It was an important step, although in theory a small one, for the virus already was adapted to growth in chick embryo mashed up in a flask.

At this point, Max Theiler, the shy, creative laboratory scientist, ceased to be a central figure in the vaccine story. Clinical trials and mass application of a vaccine were not in Theiler's line of basic research. This was a bit of Theiler luck; the history of vaccine-making, including yellow fever, shows that the task of saving humanity can become a troublesome business, particularly if one is bitten too deeply by the desire to be a benefactor of mankind. For this altogether noble and prideful aspiration, yellow fever would exact a terrible price of one more man.

30

Benefactors of Mankind

Fred Soper was still fighting *Aëdes aegypti* mosquitoes in Brazil. With yellow fever coming out of the jungles, a good vaccine offered him a new hope. "We will have it in a million people in a year," said Soper when he dropped in on Theiler.

Theiler was frankly shocked. The thought was enough to drive an experimentalist deeper into laboratory and library. Many problems have to be solved in moving a vaccine from a *tour de force* at a lab bench into a manufacturing process that will produce one million doses, all alike, all safe, all effective. To take the lead in making this kind of contribution to the health of humanity means the acceptance of a tremendous responsibility. It takes a different kind of creativity, the creativity of successful executive management, of competent individual decision and action, of cool judgment often based on nothing more than good intuition—all possibly motivated by a love of power or mastery—in this case the power to do good by mastering yellow fever.

Edward Jenner seemed to exhibit some of this urge

to glory when he visualized himself as a benefactor of mankind in these words:

"The joy I felt at the prospect before me of being the instrument destined to take away from the world one of its greatest calamities, blended with the fond hope of enjoying independence and domestic peace and happiness, was often so excessive, that in pursuing my favourite subject among the meadows, I have sometimes found myself in a kind of reverie."

Maybe what a man hears inside of him is like the "Ode to Joy" chorus from Beethoven's *Ninth Symphony*. In this ecstasy, it is easy to overlook the penalties that may attend any slip-up or failure.

The International Health Division's development of the 17D vaccine was a team effort, in which all seventy-five members of the staff and their technicians and secretaries, too, could take justifiable pride. Administratively, however, the moving spirit was Dr. Wilbur A. Sawyer. The ultimate responsibility for what was done or not done with the vaccine rested with him. Sawyer wanted it this way.

After leaving the laboratories and becoming involved in directing the I.H.D.'s far-flung affairs, he kept in close touch, often going over from the Foundation office in Rockefeller Center to the Institute to see how his successor, Johannes Bauer, and the rest were doing. He and Bauer had a close working relationship. Sawyer gave and Bauer carried out orders in the laboratory research program.

When the gentlemanly, literate Raymond B. Fosdick became president of the Foundation in 1936, he and John D. Rockefeller, Jr., chairman of the Board of Trustees, heard the vaccine story from Sawyer and applauded his sense of mission.

Sawyer personified professional competence. A medium-sized, bald man with steel-rimmed glasses and honest, Anglo-Saxon face, then in his late fifties, he spoke and wrote in good sentences and exuded integrity and dignity. Son of a Methodist clergyman, twice a Harvard graduate (A.B., 1902; M.D., 1906), he offered impeccable education and experience. He had been secretary of the California State Board of Health and a professor in hygiene and preventive medicine at the University of California, had fought venereal disease with the United States Army and the American Social Hygiene Association before joining the International Health Division staff in 1919. Like Russell, he had a strong leaning toward laboratory research in specific diseases and built his program and staff around the laboratory.

Regarded by his colleagues as somewhat cold and unbending, certainly a man of reserve, sometimes of overpowering reticence, Sawyer commanded respect from those above him and loyalty from those below. Here, then, we must understand, was a man who was in his time the flower of public health, medical science, and private philanthropy.

Sawyer and Soper agreed that the first place to conquer yellow fever was in Brazil and that Hugh Smith should go down and direct the development of the vaccine and field trials there. Sawyer instructed Smith to go slow—play it safe.

In the laboratory of the Cooperative Yellow Fever Service in Rio, Dr. Henrique A. Penna became Smith's Brazilian counterpart. They made a one-shot vaccine, seeding the tissue-culture 17D virus into hatching hens' eggs. The living embryos were removed in a week, ground up, placed in normal human serum, centrifuged, and filtered—the clear, cell-free fluid becoming the vaccine. The fluid was then frozen and reduced to a dried state for preservation until used. Samples meanwhile were tested in mice and monkeys. At the time of vaccination, the virus was mixed with distilled water and injected under the skin of the arm in a dose of 0.5 cc.

Smith and Penna began vaccinating cautiously in February—six persons, followed by eight more two weeks later and ten after another fortnight. They gradually increased their experimental groups and by September the Cooperative Yellow Fever Service offered the vaccine for routine clinical trial anywhere. Vaccinations by the end of 1937 totaled 38,000, mainly among workers on the coffee fazendas.

More than one million Brazilians were vaccinated in 1938, at a cost of eight or nine cents per person. The vaccine was used in combating current epidemics of jungle yellow fever. After ten days, it protected at least 95 percent of those receiving it; there was not, of course, enough time to tell how long the immunity would last (it was placed eventually at six and later ten years' minimum).

They kept a watch out for serum hepatitis, as it became known later. Findlay had called Theiler and Smith's attention to this hazard when they visited him in London in 1936. Nothing specific was known, but there was a general awareness of a disease or diseases called catarrhal jaundice, epidemic jaundice, infective hepatitis, and acute yellow atrophy of the liver. Findlay had been vaccinating Britons going to Africa with 17E virus and human immune serum. He had a young doctor in the hospital with jaundice following yellow-fever vaccination. Had they seen any cases like that?

Lloyd had brought the 17E virus to Rio and combined it with hyper-immune monkey serum in 1936. He found that one of every three persons thus vaccinated developed jaundice. It was later noted that Lloyd had a severe case of jaundice at the time he was making the vaccine.

Meanwhile, Findlay and Fred O. MacCallum counted nearly a hundred cases of hepatitis in upwards of 5,000 Europeans who had been vaccinated with Sawyer's and Lloyd's earlier vaccines combined with human immune serum. The jaundice these men developed could hardly be symptomatic of the quick-striking yellow fever, inasmuch as the infection came from five weeks to seven months after vaccination. Meanwhile they had developed an immunity to yellow fever.

It was a big mystery and not an easy one to solve, because of the time gap between presumed cause and effect, and because no one had isolated the causative agent. The medical profession in general knew nothing about the subject. It wasn't in the textbooks. In 1938, Soper was listening when Findlay, at a tropical medicine meeting in London, advanced knowledge a bit:

"The evidence . . . indicates that we are dealing with another virus introduced into the yellow fever tissue culture with apparently normal human serum. This virus is similar to, and probably identical with, the virus of epidemic catarrhal jaundice or . . . infective hepatitis."

This was something to think about. So was the assumption that Findlay and MacCallum offered as to when and how contamination took place. Human serum was used in the yellow-fever vaccine at two points, in the vital fluids placed in the flask to bathe the cultured tissues and in the liquid vaccine before it was put into ampules. They believed that contamination occurred when infected serum was put in the tissue culture and that the

hepatitis and yellow-fever viruses multiplied there together.

Soper and his Yellow Fever Service ran through
1,300,000 vaccinations with 17D without a bobble as
far as safety was concerned. It was a rare person who had
enough reaction to miss so much as a day's work. After
the Findlay scare, another precaution was taken at his
suggestion, beginning in 1938. Just in case some of the
blood donors might be carrying hepatitis virus, all
blood serum used in making the vaccine was heated to
about 133°F. for thirty minutes, subsequently increased
to an hour, on the assumption that this mild pasteuriza-
tion would kill the hepatitis virus, as it did other viruses.

There was no further question of post-vaccination
jaundice in Brazil until November 1939, when it was
reported in Campos, state of Rio de Janeiro. One person
died about five months after vaccination, autopsy showing subacute yellow atrophy of the liver. Dr. J. Austin
Kerr, who had replaced Smith, asked Dr. John P.
Fox of the I.H.D. staff to do the laboratory studies.
There were 140 similar cases including the one death.
Infectious hepatitis was common in Brazil and it could
have been that the outbreak was purely coincidental,
yet all cases seemed to be associated with one vaccine
lot. Fox found that while the human serum added to
this vaccine had been heat-treated, the virus came from a
culture line in which human serum had been used without being heated.

The number of Brazilians vaccinated rose to
1,900,000 by May 1940. Then post-vaccination jaundice
again stilled the shouts of joy. Espírito Santo had felt an
urgent need for protection against jungle yellow fever,

there having been more than 1,000 cases from December 1939 to May 1940. On May 14, Kerr received a telegram from Victoria telling of widespread jaundice associated with two lots of vaccine.

Soper and his staff had a busy summer. Kerr was in immediate charge of the vaccine program. He faced a familiar dilemma among public health officers. His primary responsibility, he felt, was to deliver the vaccine to the people; after all, Brazil regarded yellow fever as its No. 1 health problem. Therefore, he at first concentrated on weeding out the lots of vaccine that seemed to be contaminated. He did not halt the vaccination program, but in the next two months put most of his vaccinating teams to work investigating jaundice in persons already vaccinated. In fact, he moved practically the entire laboratory staff in Rio to Victoria to make epidemiological studies. Kerr and Soper kept Sawyer informed in long letters and diary notes.

Fox, an outstanding investigator, had the complicated facts lined up by September. He counted 1,072 cases of post-vaccination jaundice traceable to 3 out of 265 lots of vaccine. There were 24 vaccine-related deaths. The worst lot produced a jaundice incidence of 7.6 percent. The puzzling thing was the extreme variability within any one of the contaminated lots. The jaundice hit harder among poor country people, it seemed.

Fox leaned toward a "double agent" theory—that something in the vaccine and something in the environment worked together. But there was no direct evidence on either agent. As to the vaccine contaminant, he preferred the Findlay assumption that it was a virus originating in human serum but perpetuated in the tissue culture. It could not be in the added human plasma, he felt, because that was heat-treated, unless the heat was not killing all the virus.

In the face of a clear and present danger of this kind, the public health officer must act as if any possibility is true until it can be ruled out. A big question mark hung over the apparently normal blood donors, no matter when the hepatitis-contaminated serum was introduced in the yellow-fever vaccine, before or after culturing. Attempts to isolate the hepatitis virus in either patients or animals failed.

On August 21, 1940, Kerr suggested to Fox that he try making a serum-free vaccine again. Fox had made one unsuccessful attempt to do so the year before. It seemed to him that, although Bauer's earlier experience had shown either human or animal blood plasma was needed to keep the virus alive, it should survive in chick-embryo juice, just as it came from the egg. There should be enough protein there.

While Fox was experimenting, Penna spoke for Brazil on September 3. He said that all vaccination should stop until they had a product in which they had confidence. Penna himself had little doubt that the serum was to blame. Soper, Kerr, and Fox agreed. Vaccination was halted.

During the fall, Fox worked out a chick-embryo vaccine "cooked in its own juice," as it were, and mastered the extremely complicated technique of moving it through the freezing and drying stages and thence back to a liquid state, all without losing virus vitality. He was satisfied that he had conquered the protein problem, and that a newly obtained New York strain of 17D was itself uncontaminated. He made a report of his technique to Sawyer and Bauer. It was not published. Soper authorized Kerr to start a new vaccination program with serum-free vaccine in December 1940, the beginning of the yellow-fever season.

Soper's decision, he said, was influenced not only by the accumulated evidence in Brazil but something he and Smith had uncovered earlier. Years before, Theiler's father, Sir Arnold Theiler, in South Africa, had observed a somewhat similar jaundice, often fatal, in horses following use of an immune serum-and-live-virus vaccine against African horse sickness. Sir Arnold saw no further cases of jaundice when the vaccine was modified and the serum left out.

All this was more or less a dress rehearsal for what was to come in the United States. There the I.H.D. laboratory was the only producer of yellow-fever vaccine and, in the course of making something approaching a quarter million doses of a serum vaccine, had encountered no trouble. This vaccine was administered to people headed overseas: missionaries, airlines pilots and other employees, businessmen, and government officials. Normal plasma for this vaccine usually was obtained in rotation from nine professional donors sent over to the laboratory by the Blood Transfusion Betterment Association in New York City and bled on the spot. The blood from a single donor was then used in making a single batch of vaccine. This point later took on some significance.

The picture completely changed in the next year. As the United States began preparing for war, Colonel James S. Simmons, chief of the Preventive Medicine Service in the Army Surgeon General's Office, in June 1940 obtained from the National Research Council the recommendation that all military personnel in or going into the tropics be immunized against yellow fever.

Need for this protection was soon dramatized by reports from the Nuba Mountains of the Anglo-Egyptian Sudan of one of the largest yellow-fever epidemics in modern times. This epidemic reportedly struck 15,000 Nubans and cost 1,500 lives, but case estimates ran as high as 40,000.

Sawyer agreed to meet the government's yellow-fever vaccine needs on an emergency basis, but recommended to Surgeon General Thomas Parran (1892-1968) that the Public Health Service establish a laboratory for large-scale, long-range production of the vaccine. Meanwhile Sawyer constructed a vaccine laboratory in the North Building of the Rockefeller Institute in September 1940 to make both yellow-fever and influenza vaccine for Army use. Dr. Kenneth Goodner (1902-1967) from the Rockefeller Institute was hired to direct it, under Bauer.

It was Sawyer's decision, with Bauer's full agreement, to stick to what for them was the tried-and-true method of making 17D vaccine—with human serum—despite the reports from Brazil and the experimental shift there to a serum-free vaccine, a move made without Sawyer's authorization. Meanwhile in New York, Theiler and Goodner began experimenting with a serum-free vaccine themselves.

By January 1941, the Rockefeller Foundation was making 50,000 doses of yellow-fever vaccine a week in New York. This did not strike Simmons as enough. He called Parran and asked him what he was doing about manufacturing yellow-fever vaccine. The Public Health Service planned a vaccine laboratory at Hamilton, Montana. (It was not in full operation until September 1941.) Parran told Dr. Andrew J. Warren, acting director while Sawyer was in Europe, that the Public Health Service was negotiating with some of the pharmaceutical companies to make the vaccine—at about one dollar a dose.

Warren was horrified. The I.H.D. was making the vaccine for two or three cents a dose. Secondly, the plan would mean bringing a procession of workers from commercial firms into the laboratory at the Rockefeller Institute to train them. Thirdly, it would take a pharmaceutical company some time to meet requirements and deliver a satisfactory vaccine. "Our new laboratory can manufacture yellow-fever vaccine faster than the Army can inject it," Warren told Parran. Bauer completely agreed.

Warren told Raymond Fosdick, the president, that the Foundation could meet the entire need for yellow-fever vaccine if it saw fit. The idea appealed to Fosdick. The Foundation was much interested in how it could best contribute to the war effort in the health field, and in fact that was why Sawyer was in Europe, to find ways. When Fosdick went to Washington the first week of February 1941 to discuss with Vice-President Henry Wallace the development of an agricultural program in Mexico, he also dropped by to see Dr. Warren Draper, acting Surgeon General of the Public Health Service. Fosdick said that the Rockefeller Foundation would manufacture all the vaccine the United States government needed—free of charge.

It was a decision in the great tradition of Frederick Gates and Wickliffe Rose—spontaneous, magnanimous, bold, and unhampered by too much knowledge, experience, or administrative soul-searching. Years later Warren recalled that he was proud to be an instrument in it.

Consequently, Wilbur Sawyer found himself captain of a vaccine industry when he returned to New York

on March 10, 1941. If he objected to the role, or disagreed
with the decision, presented to him as an accomplished
fact, no record of it has been found in his diary or elsewhere, although, according to Warren, he did find bitter
occasion a year or two later to say, "It wouldn't have
happened if I had been home." Sawyer was soon in conference with Fred Soper and Hugh Smith, who had arrived from Colombia the same day Sawyer got back from
England, but there is no record that they discussed the
plan to make vaccine for the Army and Navy, the hepatitis problem in Brazil, or the use of a serum-free vaccine. Indeed, Sawyer's diary for 1940 and 1941 nowhere
mentions the hepatitis or human serum problems.

This seems curious in retrospect. Theiler and Goodner were strongly suspicious of a random contamination
of human blood by hepatitis virus, and knew it could
happen not merely in Brazil but anywhere. Goodner
talked to Bauer, and Theiler talked to Sawyer. The latter were neighbors in Hastings-on-Hudson, and often
rode the train into New York City together. Naturally,
they talked vaccine.

Sawyer had no objection to laboratory experiments
with a serum-free vaccine but said that there had not
been enough field testing of this vaccine to determine its
stability and potency and hence to justify a change in
the manufacturing process. To wait for adequate field
testing would mean a delay in protecting American soldiers against yellow fever and Simmons did not want
any delays.

"You are courting disaster," said Theiler mildly
at one point.

"No, we have a good vaccine," Sawyer replied in
effect. "We have had no difficulty with it here in New
York. We will leave it as it is."

By July 1941, Sawyer could also point out that Kerr and Fox were in trouble again in Brazil. Since changing their 17D strain and eliminating the blood plasma, they were getting some encephalitis following vaccination. As a matter of fact, Fox had not finished writing up his hepatitis investigation before having to start another intensive investigation. In sum, more than 200 had brain inflammation among 55,000 persons vaccinated. One had died. A substrain of 17D virus apparently had reverted to neurotropic type. The vaccination program again was stopped while the manufacturing technique was reviewed, with the result that only 200,000 Brazilians received the serum-free vaccine in 1941. No errors of technique could be found. When the neurotropic strains were thrown out, the trouble with encephalitis ended. In the absence of human serum, there was no further hepatitis.

There was a good deal of logic in Sawyer's position. What had happened in Brazil was by no means clear to everyone. It was hard to believe they were not doing something wrong down there. They had had a lot of trouble. Everyone believed that heat of 133° or so should kill the hepatitis virus in any human serum added to the vaccine. (Everyone believed wrong, of course, but it was several years before it was established that heating in the order of 176°F. was necessary to kill this virus!)

Findlay's theory seemed a reasonable deduction— that the contaminant must be introduced in a certain tissue culture and be passed on through subcultures. The problem was thus one of starting vaccine manufacture with a pure strain, and Sawyer was sure Bauer had one. Bauer was sure also.

Unfortunately, thinking of this sort lent itself to a

low index of suspicion in regard to blood; the I.H.D. vaccine laboratory now needed it in far greater quantities than the New York "Better Blood" association could provide. The laboratory had a requirement for fifteen to twenty pints a week and this eventually increased to thirty and even fifty. It seemed desirable not to use Red Cross blood collected from any Tom, Dick, or Harry, but to get it from a group under some sort of continued observation, as the professional donors had been. Dr. Thomas B. Turner, professor of bacteriology at the Johns Hopkins School of Hygiene and Public Health, a former I.H.D. man, offered the solution. The medical students, interns, nurses, and laboratory technicians of Johns Hopkins Hospital would be happy to be bled and be paid for it. One could scarcely imagine a healthier young group or one more deserving of the cash.

White leghorn hatching eggs were obtained from New Jersey at the rate of 10,000 a week for virus production.

In the sixteen months ending in April 1942, the International Health Division furnished seven million doses of yellow-fever vaccine to the United States Army and Navy, the British in Africa, and to others. The Army was the biggest consumer. It vaccinated troops headed for the tropics intensively in November and December of 1941, and in early 1942 began immunizing all troops against yellow fever. This was an adequate indicator of the degree of confidence that Surgeon General James C. Magee and his staff had in the I.H.D. vaccine.

They, too, had a low index of suspicion. Following Pearl Harbor, Soper was in Washington to confer on another matter. He went by to see Colonel Simmons. "I suppose Sawyer told you about the trouble that we had in Brazil," Soper said to Simmons. Simmons had not been informed. Soper then filled him in. Reflecting on the Army's decision to vaccinate against yellow-fever, Soper said: "It was a sound decision on the whole, but you don't make it without recognizing the risk you are running."

Recognition came in March.

In February, the Surgeon General's Office received first reports of an increased incidence of catarrhal jaundice or infectious hepatitis, at first seemingly limited to posts in the western United States, but within four or five weeks occurring in epidemic numbers in troops as widely scattered as Panama, Hawaii, the Southwest Pacific, Alaska, Iceland, and England.

What the Army doctors saw were soldiers who had a sort of lemon-yellow look and complained of dark urine. They might, or might not, have come in on sick call several days before this, with the general complaint of "feeling lousy," with perhaps some nausea and vomiting, headache, dizziness, or weakness. Their temperatures were normal or slightly up. The sickness was usually mild, lasting about a week, but the jaundiced appearance continued for some time.

Rarely, in about two or three of every 1,000 cases, the man took a turn for the worse and died. Autopsies showed a yellow or red atrophy of the liver, definitely not yellow-fever pathology. Nor was it "Noguchi's *Leptospira*," or Weil's disease; laboratory tests ruled this out.

Infectious hepatitis is common in military experience, ranking among the five or six most important infectious diseases in a soldier's life. When the cases occur in hundreds and then thousands it becomes a serious matter. The Army doctors were at first inclined to blame civilians as the source of the current infection. Some, among the more imaginative, asked:

"Could it be the yellow-fever vaccine?"

Sawyer first learned of the Army's trouble with hepatitis on March 20, 1942, in telegrams from Drs. Karl F. Meyer and Monroe D. Eaton of the University of California. Both, like him, were consultants to the Secretary of War. Some 100 mild cases had occurred in Army camps out there about eight to ten weeks following yellow-fever vaccination. Soon Simmons was on the phone from Washington, discussing what to do. Sawyer offered to take Bauer and fly out to California and investigate. Simmons welcomed the suggestion and asked Sawyer to head an investigation team that would include Meyer and Eaton as well as others.

In the midst of the excitement, Raymond Fosdick returned to the Foundation from a trip. He had been visiting Army camps in a survey of soldiers' morale. The news left him a little cast down, but Sawyer assured him that the reported jaundice had nothing to do with the vaccine, and probably came from some civilian source of infection.

Sawyer found Meyer, himself a noted microbiologist and expert on parrot fever, more or less convinced that the jaundice in California was traceable to two lots of vaccine. Sawyer was not ready to jump to such a conclusion and set out with Army medical officers by automobile on a fast tour of posts, mainly air bases, since they had received the vaccine first. On March 23, he wired Dr. George K. Strode, acting for him in New York, that there probably was no causal relationship between the vaccine and the jaundice cases. It was possible for Fosdick and Mr. Rockefeller, Jr., to see it as good news a week later when Sawyer informed Strode of a jaundice epidemic in an institution for the mentally deficient near Pomona. "We're free," said Rockefeller. "It's not our vaccine."

Meyer and Eaton did not agree with Sawyer. As the facts piled up, they ran strongly against him. For one thing, post-vaccination jaundice turned up in the East. Drs. Kenneth Maxcy (1889-1966) and Ernest W. Goodpasture (1886-1960), both heavyweights in the field of virology, saw such cases at Jefferson Barracks, Missouri, and found evidence that the vaccine was to blame.

On April 1, twelve days after his arrival in California, Sawyer called Simmons in Washington. Sawyer suggested that it would be wise to suspend vaccination of troops under no immediate risk of exposure to yellow fever until the investigation had progressed far enough to show whether the vaccine was the source of jaundice. Simmons felt that in view of the mildness of the cases and in view of the need for yellow-fever immunization, routine vaccination should continue until there was strong evidence against it.

Within the next ten days, however, the accumulated evidence was such that Simmons was persuaded. In the first place, there was no general increase of jaundice among civilians in California or elsewhere. Cases among civilian workers on Army posts were rare. The reports of cases among vaccinated men continued to mount, reaching 3,400 in the United States, Hawaii, and Panama Canal Zone. (The first peak in early April was followed by a much higher one in the latter part of June.) A concentration of cases in relation to certain lots of vaccine—a lot was 80,000 doses—was definitely established. (Finally, nine out of 117 lots were found to be the source of most cases.)

On April 13, Sawyer telephoned Simmons the findings of his team, recommending temporary suspension of the I.H.D. vaccine lots under suspicion and a shift meanwhile to Public Health Service vaccine from the Rocky Mountain Laboratory in Hamilton. Two days later the Surgeon General so ordered. Captain C. S. Stephenson, Navy Medical Chief, said, as far as the Navy was concerned, it was going ahead; it had had no trouble.

Serum-free vaccine now acquired official merit. Bauer was now more inclined to listen to Theiler and Goodner. They said it was simple to make a good vaccine without using blood plasma, and it would take only two weeks to switch production over. Strode, receiving this proposal from Bauer, called Sawyer in San Francisco. Unquestionably, serum-free vaccine would eliminate one possible source of infection. Sawyer still hesitated to take the step, but later wired: STRODE . . . ON AFTERTHOUGHT WILLING HAVE HUMAN SERUM OMITTED FROM VACCINE PROVIDED SATISFACTORY PRODUCT AS TEMPORARY EXPERIMENTAL PROCEDURE. . . . The experiment is still going on, for nobody returned to human serum after the Army hepatitis incident.

After June 1, the Army used nothing but serum-free yellow-fever vaccine and, in the remainder of 1942, the I.H.D. vaccine laboratory made 4 million doses of it for the Army, Navy, and others. What before had seemed such a problematical course became, after the disaster predicted by Theiler, too, too obvious.

Speculation about all the angles of "Rockefeller disease," as serum hepatitis became known in the Army, never has quite ceased, particularly among researchers in preventive medicine and serum hepatitis in particular. The curiosity has at times soured into criticism because I.H.D. publications skirted frank exposition of the incident in the hope of saving embarrassment to the various authorities involved.

The Army officially recorded "The Serum Hepatitis Epidemic of 1942" as the most extensive in military history. For the entire year, in the continental United States and all theaters of operations, there were 49,233 reported cases of infectious and serum hepatitis, and eighty-four deaths. The "vast majority" were attributed to the vaccine-borne infection. About 70 percent of the cases were within the United States. Following the trouble, the Army stopped vaccinating everyone in uniform against yellow fever, restricting it to those in or headed for tropical areas.

Sawyer and his team published a 200-page report of their investigation in 1944 in the *American Journal of Hygiene*, shortly after he retired in anticipation of his sixty-fifth birthday.

Bauer had no difficulty in finding where the hepatitis virus came from. He knew that by May 19, 1942. About 2 percent of the several hundreds of "presumably healthy" medical students, interns, nurses, and technicians who had given blood at Johns Hopkins were found to have a history of jaundice within one to twenty years before. A few had the disease more recently—for example, J.F., a physician, was convalescing from catarrhal jaundice and still yellow at the time he gave blood on January 27, 1942. Through pooling, his blood was spread over five lots, or 400,000 doses, of vaccine. Bauer's study showed that little thought previously had been given to the clinical history of the blood donors.

Sawyer accepted full responsibility for what happened, rather than pass any part of it to various persons in a position to share it. He became a target for harsh criticism not only for his error of judgment but for not having shared the responsibility of decision with others.

Fosdick recalled the spring of 1942 as "the most anxious days I ever went through." Once the awful facts were known, he went to Mr. Rockefeller, Jr., and told him the whole story. Rockefeller reassured him and said, "Well, we will work it out. We have a good team over there," referring to the I.H.D. Laboratories.

There are lessons aplenty to be learned in the story of human error connected with yellow fever that began with Benjamin Rush.

One, a surprise, was that out of tragedy came a new contribution of scientific knowledge. Now the medical profession knew that there was not only infectious hepatitis but also serum hepatitis and that a "fairly large proportion of normal persons may act as carriers," to quote Sawyer. As dried plasma, made from the pooling of the blood of many persons, came into wide use during World War II, the problem of serum hepatitis presented itself on a much wider scale. The Army Medical Corps was able to differentiate it from the epidemics of infectious hepatitis that also went on. It presently abandoned the use of pooled plasma, on the kind of evidence first generated in Sawyer's report.

Paradoxically, MacCallum, who shared credit with Findlay as the first to identify a filterable virus as the cause of post-vaccination hepatitis, was still making a vaccine containing human serum when the epidemic broke out in the United States. Indeed, he did not abandon use of serum in British vaccine until January 1943, after running into the same contamination problem in October 1942, months after serum-free vaccine was being used among American troops.

When the I.H.D. Laboratories closed the vaccine-making program in 1947, it had distributed 28 million doses, 18 million to the Armed Forces, at a cost to the Foundation of 2.2. cents per dose, including overhead, and no expense to the thirty-three different agencies using this vaccine.

The Rockefeller Foundation spent more in fighting yellow fever than any other specific disease, more than $8 million from 1916 to 1949. This was exclusive of more than $4 million in staff salaries and expenses allocated to yellow-fever activities.

Almost overlooked in reflections on the 1942 serum hepatitis epidemic was the strategic value of the vaccine—to protect the hundreds of thousands of American troops moving in and out of Central and South American and Caribbean jungle yellow-fever zones, and particularly along the supply lines across Africa to the Middle and Far East. In four years of war, not one case of yellow fever was reported in an American soldier. Yellow fever did occur sporadically in the areas in which some troops were stationed both in South America and Africa.

Meanwhile the French stuck to their own vaccine and launched a great immunization program in West Africa. Using the Theiler neurotropic strain, they had no problem with serum hepatitis. Their vaccine did not use human serum. In 1939, Peltier and Durieux introduced a new type of "Dakar scratch vaccine," offering combined protection against smallpox *and* yellow fever.

The two viruses, the super-potent French strain generated in mouse brains and the vaccinia, were scratched into the arm and then covered with a gummy substance to keep them from drying out. The appeal of the scratch method was at least twofold. No complicated

tissue cultures or egg incubators were required to prop-
agate the virus—only mice. The scratch infection did
away with the need of syringes, hollow needles, and ster-
ilization apparatus, a great gain where universal vaccination of a primitive people was the aim. Also it killed
two big disease birds with one stone.

Beginning in 1940, the Institut Pasteur in Dakar
vaccinated with this new type of vaccine on a wholesale basis and, by 1953, had provided more than
56 million doses. This was more than two per person
for the population of French African territories south
of the Sahara. As a result, yellow fever disappeared,
except for the rare case, although aegypti mosquitoes
were virtually everywhere and monkeys and mosquitoes in the jungle were found to be infected.

Presently, however, the French had second thoughts
on the old problem of post-vaccination encephalitis,
which had turned Theiler against his neurotropic strain
of virus. During a shortage of 17D vaccine in Latin
America, Costa Rica in 1951 imported some of the Dakar
scratch vaccine. Careful observation showed that it
failed to immunize some adults and produced fifteen
cases of encephalitis in children, five of them fatal. The
following year, extensive use of the Dakar vaccine in Nigeria resulted in something over eighty cases of encephalitis with forty deaths. Use of the vaccine in the Belgian
Congo in 1958 resulted in still more encephalitis.

It was observed that post-vaccination encephalitis
occurred almost entirely in children under ten, with the
result that in 1960 the French came to the decision to
limit use of the Dakar vaccine to adults and children over
ten.

This, of course, meant leaving the most threatened
portion of the population unprotected and resulted, at

the end of 1965, in a severe outbreak of yellow fever, almost certainly transmitted by aegypti, in the Diourbel and M'backe regions of Senegal. The last large outbreak of yellow fever in Senegal had been in 1927, with 135 reported deaths. The 1965 epidemic produced 140 deaths, mostly in children under ten.

Following this setback, Senegalese health officials undertook their first mass vaccination of small children with 17D vaccine, using a new jet-pressure gun that fires the vaccine dose through the skin without breaking it, in place of the customary syringe and needle. Some 130,000 were vaccinated with no reported bad effects. In contrast, as a final demonstration of the danger of the neurotropic strain of virus, 90,000 children under ten received the Dakar vaccine. Two hundred forty were hospitalized with encephalitis and twenty-five died.

In modern experience, the 17D vaccine is not entirely free of this danger in small children, but the cases of encephalitis following its use are extremely rare.

With the development of a safe and effective vaccine, there was a rather common presumption that yellow fever had become a thing of the past. It became so for the Foundation, which was moving on to other programs. Indeed, thanks mainly to the partial eradication of *Aëdes aegypti*, there are today but few cases of yellow fever in the Americas. In thirteen years, 1947-1959, there were 1,784 cases reported in the Western Hemisphere, an average of 137 a year. All were jungle yellow fever except three cases among eighteen in Trinidad in 1954. Yellow fever is not a major international threat to people's health today, as compared to such diseases as tuberculosis, malaria, nutritional deficiencies, the diarrheas and pneumonias of children, and influenza.

Soper, however, sharply protests such downgrading. Yellow fever is not a minor problem to him. He points, for example, to the epidemic of yellow fever that moved through Ethiopia from the Sudan in 1961 and 1962. Rough estimates of deaths ran as high as 15,000. Clearly, yellow fever is not a dead issue.

It is natural to ask why the 17D vaccine has not been used on a saturation scale in the Americas and Africa to lock yellow fever out of the human blood stream, particularly since there has been an inclination to accent the vaccine as a landmark in the conquest of the disease.

The answer is a complex one. In the first place, there are technical difficulties, such as the tendency of the 17D virus to lose its potency in hot climates, where refrigeration may sometimes be faulty. "These difficulties," as Soper says, "are real but not insurmountable."

But the human equation so far does seem to be insurmountable. The greatest obstacle to systematic and complete vaccination against yellow fever in the tropics has been a lack of public interest. Problems of education, economics, and manpower aside, the psychological problem is a tough one. As has been seen in the United States, people are prone to celebrate the conquest of a disease at the time they receive the good news that it is possible, rather than when conquest is complete. Soper decries the prematurity of repeated claims of conquest since Gorgas's initial victory in Havana, and objects to the use of such words as "victory," "triumph," or "conquest" in connection with yellow fever.

But there is a greater paradox here than that of false hope or all-too-human misunderstanding. The most effective stimulus to public attack on a disease is a present danger from that disease: as the disease declines so does public concern, sometimes at a more rapid rate than the reduction in the number of cases remaining. This has been so commonly observed it is virtually a theorem of public health.

Only where jungle fever is on the move has it been easy to get the money, staff, vaccine, automobiles, and equipment to undertake mass vaccination. Further, while vaccination protects the individual indefinitely, it offers only a temporary protection for a population inasmuch as a new, susceptible generation is born day by day; in addition, there may be susceptible newcomers to the area. On the other hand, as long as it is impossible to vaccinate every monkey in the trees or kill every forest mosquito, the vaccine is the one means of protection from jungle yellow fever.

31

Doctor Sawyer's Ordeal

In 1951, Max Theiler, the South African of Swiss parentage from Westchester County, New York, who got his education in London and did his work in Boston and New York, was awarded the Nobel Prize by the Carolinian Institute of Sweden for his discoveries in yellow fever.

Otherwise, it was a bad year for the International Health Division. Originally, I. H. D. prophets of world health had considered their mission to be the application of existing medical and public health knowledge in backward areas. Its doctors were driven, for one thing, by the intention of eradicating—totally uprooting—certain diseases of mankind, most of all hookworm disease, malaria, and yellow fever. In each instance, however, existing knowledge proved insufficient and their gains depended on new discoveries. The gap was not between knowing and doing, as Frederick Gates and Wickliffe Rose thought, but between what science knew and what it needed to know, as Frederick Russell said.

What the followers of Rose and the Aristotelian precept of learning by doing demonstrated was that the priceless ingredients of action were not so much their scientific knowledge and technical skills but their imagination, enthusiasm, and initiative, reinforced by hard work, patience, and perseverance. With few exceptions, they learned humility; this made them much admired, everywhere they went, as the friendly Americans. The lesson they learned was sometimes lost on others, unfortunately.

The I.H.D. as an identified, quasi-autonomous, and unique institution, came to an end in April 1951. The Foundation chose to terminate it for a number of reasons. One was that its overarching mission of leadership in promotion of international health might be said to be complete. The World Health Organization was established in 1948, and in many ways this United Nations agency constituted a fulfillment of private philanthropy's objective—the United States and other governments now appeared awake to their responsibilities in international health.

Also, it was now evident that classic public health methods, primarily directed to the prevention of infectious diseases, were not designed to cope with some of the world's most pressing health problems. To some extent the result of the disruption of economic systems and educational institutions by politics, power struggles, violence, and war, these problems included hunger and overpopulation and, in the poor countries, a lack of money to raise the standard of living.

Wilbur Sawyer, who had retired in 1944, said as much when he wrote in the *New England Journal of Medicine* at the beginning of 1951: "Early in the half-century it was surmised that improvement in health would promptly be followed by increased production, and a better economic position would result in fuller so-

cial development. Probably, the health work would have
had this effect except for the periodic setbacks by war
and by interference with international trade, travel and
communications. The problem is much broader than
health, which cannot flourish in an adverse socioeconomic environment."

These were wise words, many times since recon-
firmed, from a man whose passing, at the end of 1951,
was in certain aspects more tragic than that of anyone
who gave his life in the fight against yellow fever. In
an interview in 1964, the year before her own death,
Mrs. Sawyer was dramatically blunt: "The award of the
Nobel Prize to Max Theiler killed my husband."

Anyone, of course, may dispute the judgment of the
Nobel Prize judges, and a few have, with some reason.
Yet it is hard for the disinterested observer to find fault
with the cablegram that Theiler received at the I.H.D.
Laboratories on October 13, 1951. It said he had been
awarded the Nobel Prize in physiology and medicine
"for your discoveries concerning yellow fever and how
to combat it." As brought out later in the presenta-
tion at Stockholm, the award took into account Theiler's
first attenuation of the virus at Harvard, the subsequent development of vaccines with this neurotropic
strain both by the Rockefeller and Dakar Institut Pasteur groups, and then his production, together with
Lloyd and Ricci, of the 17D strain. The citation also mentioned the "comprehensive and fruitful work in combating yellow fever" carried out by the I.H.D. for more
than a generation; it said Theiler occupied "an especially
prominent place" among the many who had made contributions.

True, not every I.H.D. staff member was happy to
see one man singled out of what so obviously had been a

team effort. Johannes Bauer, then still alive, had been the principal investigator in the isolation of the Asibi strain from monkeys and its identification as a filterable virus. It was Sawyer who introduced the first effective vaccine, the one that put an end to yellow fever among laboratory workers. It was Hugh Smith, working with Theiler, who first called attention to the mutation that yielded the 17D vaccine.

There was another way of looking at the matter. The Nobel Prize Committee said it had based the award not on originality, for Jenner and Pasteur had anticipated Theiler, but on service to mankind. In the control of urban yellow fever in the Western Hemisphere, the role of the vaccine was secondary to the fight against mosquitoes; Fred Soper was the strong man in that story. As a matter of fact, one Pan-American health meeting had considered a resolution respectfully recommending to the Nobel people that they award the prize to two men, Sawyer and Soper. The recommendation was never made, for the resolution bogged down in a Latin American debate over what other names should be added.

The case for sharing, however, apparently was not uppermost in Wilbur Sawyer's mind. He had led the laboratory attack on yellow fever for sixteen years, and indeed had bent the I.H.D. organization toward the conquest of this disease. To be sure, out of faith in the creativity of the human mind, science honors moments of discovery rather than of superior administration. But Sawyer regarded himself as a scientist as well as the moving spirit, as indeed he was, in the development of the 17D vaccine. His colleagues were in agreement on this point.

As for the hepatitis contamination of the yellow-fever vaccine, it would come as a deep wound to the professional pride of any responsible man. It remained in the record as an ugly scar on a magnificent effort to do good. Intramurally, there was harsh criticism of Sawyer's stubborn insistence on use of human serum in the vaccine. Sawyer accepted the responsibility and swallowed the criticism, but he could not admit the fact that he had made an error in judgment.

When they both were living in retirement in Berkeley, Lewis Hackett would come to tea with Wilbur Sawyer and they would discuss the vaccine. Sawyer continued to defend the course he had followed, on the ground that earlier evidence suggesting that human serum might harbor the agent of hepatitis was not at all convincing. As Hackett explained to Soper: "Being right and wrong was a moral question with Sawyer. To be wrong was immoral, and Wilbur was a moral man."

"A measure of the man," Soper wrote Hackett, "can be seen from the fact that when trouble came, Sawyer shouldered the blame and took all of the censure without at any time permitting . . . others in the lab to become involved. . . . If he takes the blame, Wilbur should also participate in the credit. . . ."

While she charged that the award of the prize to Theiler killed her husband, Margaret Sawyer, herself a bacteriologist, apparently meant to be rhetorical. She did not mean, she said, that he would not have died in due course. He had not been well. Early in 1951, he tired easily and was visibly aging.

But he then improved considerably, so much so that Mrs. Sawyer felt free to go to West Germany in the fall to be with a daughter who was expecting a baby. At the end of October, she received a cablegram saying that Dr. Sawyer was seriously ill and in the hospital.

Returning home as soon as possible, she found him on the downgrade and morbidly preoccupied.

He asked her if she had heard the news. Max Theiler had received the Nobel Prize for the yellow-fever vaccine. Sawyer said this was a denial of his entire career. *He* developed the yellow-fever vaccine.

Sawyer was puzzled about who had done this thing to him, Mrs. Sawyer went on. He felt that his scientific colleagues were rejecting him. He was deeply, terribly hurt. . . . The hepatitis incident was completely a surprise . . . entirely unexpected . . . entirely unforeseen. He had not wanted to harm anyone, he told her. Did she know of anyone he had harmed? He asked her this question over and over. There was a feeling as if he was meeting a final judgment, she said. He could not live with repudiation.

Wilbur Sawyer—"the sleepless soul that perished in his pride"—died on November 12, 1951. He was seventy-two.

Moved by his conviction that a great wrong had been done him, Mrs. Sawyer got out Sawyer's diaries, hoping to find there the explanation of his course of action in the manufacture of the vaccine. It was not there, she said. But out of love for her husband and respect for his courage and devotion to his work, she nevertheless wrote a manuscript in his defense.

What became of this manuscript? "I burned it," she said.

Missing the early lesson of yellow-fever research history—great men can make great mistakes—Sawyer fought the enemy, error, in the only way he knew how. He stood his ground and denied it access. He wanted to be a hero in the eyes of his fellow men.

In 1931, writing about recent progress in yellow-fever research, Sawyer put down the prophetic words by which he should be remembered: "The knowledge that we have of yellow fever has been purchased most dearly. It should be fully appreciated and given wide application."

SELECTED

BIBLIOGRAPHY

INDEX

Selected Bibliography

The books and articles grouped below are some of the published and, in some instances, particularly interesting sources of information on which the author has drawn.

The original portions of *The Plague Killers* were made possible through access to the annual reports, letters, memoranda, diaries, bulletins, and project reports of the Rockefeller Sanitary Commission for the Eradication of Hookworm Disease and the International Health Commission, International Health Board, and International Health Division of the Rockefeller Foundation, plus interviews with forty-five survivors among the more than four hundred public health doctors, nurses, sanitary engineers, and others who at some time ranged the earth in pursuit of Rockefeller world health aims.

Somebody at the Rockefeller Foundation—a lot of somebodies—did a monumental job of filing away old documents of all kinds in such a way that the writer usually had only to ask and he received. In only a few instances, such as the occasion when it took two weeks of corresponding and interviewing to produce the information for one paragraph—later deleted—was it necessary to dig in the fierce, unrelenting manner in which we imagine brilliant scholars of history are always digging. The material usually was in the records, in confusingly vast quantities and vastly complicated by the sprawl in time, space, and major fields of interest.

The materials left by Dr. Lewis W. Hackett, who started but did not finish writing a history of the International Health Division before his death in 1962, were of immeasurable help. They included 1,500 pages of type-written notes, innumerable hand-written notes, a large correspondence with his colleagues, and nine rough drafts of chapters.

General

CORNER, G. W. *A History of the Rockefeller Institute, 1901-1953; Origins and Growth.* New York: Rockefeller Institute Press, 1964.

CURTI, M. *American Philanthropy Abroad: A History.* New Brunswick, N.J.: Rutgers University Press, 1963.

FAIR, G. M. "Contributions to Sanitary Engineering," *Journal of the Boston Society of Civil Engineers,* 35 (1948), no. 3, section 2, 321-336.

FERRELL, J. A., and P. A. MEAD. *History of County Health Organizations in the United States, 1908-1933.* Public Health Bulletin No. 222. Washington, D.C.: U.S. Government Printing Office, 1936.

FOSDICK, R. B. *The Story of the Rockefeller Foundation.* New York: Harper & Brothers, 1952.

GOODMAN, N. M. *International Health Organizations and Their Work.* Philadelphia: Blakiston, 1952.

HEISER, V. G. *An American Doctor's Odyssey; Adventures in Forty-Five Countries.* New York: Norton, 1936.

MAY, S. "Economic Aspects of Health in Tropical Areas." In *Industry and Tropical Health,* Proceedings of the Fifth Conference of the Industrial Council for Tropical Health Sponsored by the Harvard School of Public

Health, October 29-31, 1963, in Boston. Boston: Harvard School of Public Health, 1964. Pp. 17-23.

MONYPENNY, W. F., and G. E. BUCKLE. *The Life of Benjamin Disraeli, Earl of Beaconsfield.* 2 vols. New York: Macmillan, 1929.

MORGAN, M. *Doctors to the World.* New York: The Viking Press, 1958.

MORISON, R. S. "The Concept of Eradication and Public Education," *The Pharos of Alpha Omega Alpha,* 26 (1963), no. 1, 3-7.

SEIPP, C. (ed.). *Health Care for the Community; Selected Papers of Dr. John B. Grant.* The American Journal of Hygiene Monographic Series, No. 21. Baltimore: Johns Hopkins Press, 1963.

SHATTUCK, L. *Report of a General Plan for the Promotion of Public and Personal Health, Devised, Prepared, and Recommended by the Commissioners Appointed under a Resolve of the Legislature of Massachusetts, Relating to a Sanitary Survey of the State.* Boston: Dutton & Wentworth, 1850.

SIMMONS, J. S. *Public Health in the World Today.* Cambridge, Mass.: Harvard University Press, 1949.

SMILLIE, W. G. *Public Health Administration in the United States.* New York: Macmillan, 3rd ed., 1947.

———. *Public Health: Its Promise for the Future; A Chronicle of the Development of Public Health in the United States, 1607-1914.* New York: Macmillan, 1955.

TAYLOR, C. E. "Medical Care for Developing Countries," *Atlantic Monthly,* 213 (1964), no. 1, 75-76+.

WASHBURN, B. E. *A Country Doctor in the South Mountains.* Asheville, N.C.: Stephens Press, 1955.

WILLIAMS, G. "The Rockefeller Foundation; How It Operates," *Atlantic Monthly,* 213 (1964), 106-118.

WILLIAMS, R. C. *The United States Public Health Service, 1798-1950.* Bethesda, Md.: Commissioned Officers Association of the United States Public Health Service, 1951.

WINSLOW, C. E. A. *Conquest of Epidemic Disease; A Chapter in the History of Ideas.* Princeton, N.J.: Princeton University Press, 1943.

WORLD HEALTH ORGANIZATION. *The First Ten Years of the World Health Organization.* Geneva: World Health Organization, 1958.

WRIGHT, W. H. (ed.). *Tropical Health; A Report on the Study of Needs and Resources.* Washington, D.C.: Publication No. 996, National Academy of Sciences–National Research Council, 1962.

ZINSSER, H. *Rats, Lice, and History.* Boston: Little, Brown, 1935.

Hookworm Disease

BEAVER, P. C. *Control of Soil-Transmitted Helminths.* Public Health Papers, No. 10. Geneva: World Health Organization, 1961.

CARR, H. P. "Hookworm Disease." In Tice, F., and L. H. Sloan (eds.). *Practice of Medicine.* Hagerstown, Md.: W. F. Prior & Co., Vol. V, 1958. Pp. 79-105.

HENDRICK, B. J. *The Life and Letters of Walter H. Page.* 2 vols. New York: Doubleday, 1922.

LAMBERT, S. M. *A Yankee Doctor in Paradise.* Boston: Little, Brown, 1941.

STILES, C. W. "Early History, in Part Esoteric, of the Hookworm (Uncinariasis) Campaign in Our Southern United States," *Journal of Parasitology,* 25 (1939), 283-308.

STOLL, N. R. "This Wormy World," *Journal of Parasitology,* 33 (1947), no. 1, 1-18.

———. "On Endemic Hookworm, Where Do We Stand Today?" *Experimental Parasitology,* 12 (1962), 241-252.

SULLIVAN, M. *Our Times; The United States 1900-1925.* 4 vols. New York: Scribner, 1926–1932.

WASHBURN, B. E. *As I Recall.* The Hookworm Campaigns

Initiated by the Rockefeller Sanitary Commission and
The Rockefeller Foundation in the Southern United
States and Tropical America. New York: The Rocke-
feller Foundation, 1960.

Malaria

BOYD, M. F. (ed.). *Malariology, a Comprehensive Survey of
All Aspects of This Group of Diseases from a Global
Standpoint.* 2 vols. Philadelphia and London: W. B.
Saunders, 1949.

HACKETT, L. W. "The Disappearance of Malaria in Europe
and the United States," *Rivista di Parassitologia,* XIII
(1952), no. 1, 43-56.

HACKETT, L. W. *Malaria in Europe, an Ecological Study.*
London School of Hygiene and Tropical Medicine,
Heath Clark Lectures, 1934. London: Oxford Uni-
versity Press, 1937.

LOGAN, J. A., *et al. The Sardinian Project: An Experiment
in the Eradication of an Indigenous Malarious Vector.*
American Journal of Hygiene Monographic Series,
No. 20. Baltimore: Johns Hopkins Press, 1953.

NEWMAN, P. *Malaria Eradication and Population Growth,
with Special Reference to Ceylon and British Guiana.*
Bureau of Public Health Economics, Research Series
No. 10. School of Public Health, University of Michigan, 1965.

NG, L. K. Y., and S. MUDD (eds.). *The Population Crisis:
Implications and Plans for Action.* Bloomington, Ind.:
Indiana University Press, 1965.

PAMPANA, E. J., and P. F. RUSSELL. "Malaria: A World Problem," *Chronicle of the World Health Organization,*
9 (1955), no. 2-3, 31-100.

RUSSELL, P. F. Introduction to *Communicable Diseases, Ma-
laria*: Vol. 6 of *Preventive Medicine in World War II,*
Coates, J. B., Jr., and E. C. Hoff (eds.) for the Medical
Department, United States Army. Washington, D.C.:

U.S. Government Printing Office, 1963, chap. I. Pp. 1-10.

————. *Man's Mastery of Malaria.* The London School of Hygiene and Tropical Medicine, Heath Clark Lectures, 1953. London: Oxford University Press, 1955.

RUSSELL, P. F., L. S. WEST, R. D. MANWELL, and G. MACDONALD. *Practical Malariology.* London: Oxford University Press, 2nd ed., 1963.

SNYDER, J. C. "Typhus Fever in the Second World War," *California Medicine,* 66 (1947), no. 1, 3-10.

SOPER, F. L., and D. B. WILSON. *Anopheles Gambiae in Brazil, 1930 to 1940.* New York: The Rockefeller Foundation, 1943.

Yellow Fever

AGRAMONTE, A. "The Inside Story of a Great Medical Discovery," *Scientific Monthly* (December, 1915), 209-237.

COATES, J. B., JR., and E. C. HOFF (eds.). *Personal Health Measures and Immunization. Preventive Medicine in World War II, Vol. III.* Medical Department, United States Army. Washington, D.C.: U.S. Government Printing Office, 1955.

ECKSTEIN, G. *Noguchi.* New York: Harper, 1931.

GORGAS, M. D., and B. J. HENDRICK. *William Crawford Gorgas, His Life and Work.* New York: Doubleday, 1924.

HENCH, P. S. "Walter Reed and the Conquest of Yellow Fever," *The Pharos of Alpha Omega Alpha,* 11 (1948), 8-14.

HUDSON, N. P. "Adrian Stokes and Yellow Fever Research: A Tribute," *Transactions of the Royal Society of Tropical Medicine and Hygiene,* 60 (1966), no. 2, 170-174.

KELLY, H. A. *Walter Reed and Yellow Fever.* New York: Doubleday, 2nd ed., 1906.

RIVERS, T. M., and F. L. HORSFALL, JR. (eds.). *Viral and*

Rickettsial Infections of Man. Philadelphia: Lippincott, 3rd ed., 1959.

SOPER, F. L. "The Elimination of Urban Yellow Fever in the Americas through the Eradication of Aëdes Aegypti," *American Journal of Public Health*, 53 (1963), no. 1, 7-16.

STRODE, G. K. (ed.). *Yellow Fever*. New York: McGraw-Hill, 1951.

UNITED STATES SENATE. *Yellow Fever: A Compilation of Various Publications: Results of the Work of Maj. Walter Reed, Medical Corps, United States Army, and the Yellow Fever Commission*. U.S. 61st Congress, 3rd session, Senate Document No. 822. Washington, D.C.: U.S. Government Printing Office, 1911.

WILLIAMS, G. *Virus Hunters*. New York: Knopf, 1959.

About the Author

Greer Williams, for the last thirty years, has been a science writer and "witness in the field of medicine and public health." He is now an assistant professor at Tufts University School of Medicine and assistant director for communications of the Tri-State Regional Medical Program in Massachusetts, New Hampshire, and Rhode Island.

Mr. Williams, as a writer and editor, has shown a strong tendency to be where the action is—as an information officer in aviation medicine in the Army Air Forces during World War II, as a writer consultant in American Cancer Society campaigns, in the American College of Surgeons' campaign against fee-splitting and unjustified surgery, as editor and principal author of the Joint Commission on Mental Illness and Health's report, *Action for Mental Health* (1961), and most recently in the efforts of Regional Medical Programs to improve the quality of medical care in heart disease, cancer, stroke, and related diseases.

The Plague Killers is based on hitherto unpublished material made available to him during his service as a consultant on medical and natural sciences to The Rockefeller Foundation from 1962 to 1968. He interviewed many of the doctors who took part in the health campaigns he describes.

Mr. Williams has contributed to a wide variety of magazines and journals, including the *Saturday Evening Post, Atlantic, Harper's, Science, New England Journal of Medicine,* and *Modern Hospital.* A previous book for the general reader, *Virus Hunters,* has been translated into nine languages since its publication in 1959.